Alaska Quarterly Review

Vol. 39 No. 1 & 2   ❖   ❖   Winter & Spring 2023

in collaboration with

CENTER FOR THE NARRATIVE & LYRIC ARTS
ANCHORAGE MUSEUM
UNIVERSITY OF ALASKA
ANCHORAGE

*

Alaska Quarterly Review is a journal devoted to contemporary literary art of aesthetic strength and power and also work that includes a rigorous questioning of larger societal issues. It is published twice each year in print and digital editions.

Editor Ronald Spatz **Senior Affiliate Editors** Robert Clark, Stephanie Cole, Christine Byl, Amy Meissner, Shane Castle, Carol Sturgulewski
Affiliate Editors Stacy Smith, Jamey Bradbury, Megan O'Connor, Chaun Ballard, Debra Pennington Davis, Jennifer Alessi, Alyse Knorr, Tara Ballard, Kate Partridge, Seta Melkonian, Matt Callahan, Jamilla Hagen, Ioanna-Mariia Bakulina (Web), Maggie Woda (Social Media) **Contributing Editors** Elizabeth Bradfield, Billy Collins, Olena Kalytiak Davis, Stuart Dischell, Stuart Dybek, Nancy Eimers, Patricia Hampl, Amy Hempel, Sean Hill, Jane Hirshfield, Dorianne Laux, Bonnie Nadzam, Pattiann Rogers, Michael Ryan, Peggy Shumaker, Benjamin J. Spatz
Founding Editors Ronald Spatz, James Jakob Liszka
Intern Sibongumusa Ncube **Editorial Assistant** Sheila Sine

Subscription rates: $20.00 for one year, $40.00 for two years, and $60.00 for three years. Please add $4.00 per year for Canadian subscriptions and $10.00 per year for subscriptions to all other countries. Sample copies are $9.00 for U.S. and Canada; $16.00 to all other countries. Back issue prices on request.

Submissions: The editors invite fiction, short plays, poetry, and literary nonfiction in traditional and experimental styles. Unsolicited manuscripts are read on SUBMITTABLE [*https://alaskaquarterlyreview.submittable.com/submit*]. For full submission guidelines including submission windows visit our website [*https://aqreview.org/writers-guidelines*].

Send all correspondence: Editors, *Alaska Quarterly Review* via email: [*aqr@uaa.alaska.edu*]

Website: [*http://www.aqreview.org*] **Facebook:** [*facebook.com/alaskaquarterlyreview*]
Twitter: [*AQReview*]

YouTube Channel: [*https://www.youtube.com/alaskaquarterlyreview*]

Distributors: TNG, 1955 Lake Park Drive, Ste. 400, Smyrna, GA 30080
          Media Solutions, 9632 Madison Blvd., Madison, AL 35758
          University Microfilms International, 300 North Zeeb Road,
          Ann Arbor, MI 48106

Alaska Quarterly Review is listed in *Humanities International Complete* and is a member of CLMP.

ISSN 0737-268X

About the cover and photographer
Moonrise, Parks Ridge Road, Alaska 1.5.22 © 2022 Kate Wool.

Kate Wool is an Alaska-based photographer who has had work exhibited locally, nationally, and internationally. Her publications include *Americans for the Arts*, *The Washington Post*, *Alaska Quarterly Review*, *The Art Newspaper*, *Together We Rise*, *The Women's March Organizers and Condé Nast*, and *Politico*. She was named Ruth Lister Feminist of the Year (2018) for her gun safety activism.

*

AQR
Alaska Quarterly Review

Vol. 39 No. 1 & 2   Winter & Spring 2023

CONTENTS

STORIES

song of the burning woman — ire'ne lara silva 9

Never Speak the Word Drown — Kate Blakinger 31

Sim — Alicia Oltuski 47

Ash Wednesday — Jacqueline Keren 55

Swimming Lessons — Michael Horton 66

Throwing Punches — Marlin Barton 71

Three-Season Room — Alyson Mosquera Dutemple 103

La Petite Mort — Ryan Habermeyer 115

Just This — Pamela Painter 123

ESSAYS

Hungry Ghost — May-lee Chai 139

Anufeek, Da Wuv Tonight? — DC Lambert 152

An Incision in the Reeds — Daniel Mueller 168

For Years I Said — Kate Angus 177

The Cave — Debbie Urbanski 182

LONG POEMS

Field Studies — Alison Hawthorne Deming 201

Dove of the Morning News — Bruce Bond 208

AQR
Alaska Quarterly Review

Vol. 39 No. 1 & 2   Winter & Spring 2023

POEMS

Poem in Which St. Maria Goretti Gives Lilies to Her Murderer — Amanda Auchter 221

The Tenth Time — Meryl Natchez............ 223

The Dark Air — Mariella Nigro (Translated by Jesse Lee Kercheval and Jeannine M. Pitas)....... 224

The Rough Beast Never Asked to Be Born — Alexandra Teague......... 226

'The Orange Blossom Special' (Arranged for Rome's Burning) — 228

Guardian Angel — Jenna Le 231

De Colores — Emily Schulten 232

Because There Was Nothing — Jason Tandon 234

The Glass Parrot — Deborah Brown 235

Another Dedication— After Czeslaw Milosz — Emily Franklin 236

A Brief History of Hurricanes — Sara Henning............. 238

At the Beach the Summer My Mother Files for Divorce, Deciding, After Three Years, My Father Has Left for Good — Robin Chapman 240

CNN Says Nuclear War Could Break Out at Any Moment — Julie Danho 241

Dispatch from the Events Leading Up to the End — Megan Gannon........... 242

Birds Don't Understand Us — Peter Krumbach 244

From Where I Flew — Mar Ka 245

House of Freaks — Nancy Miller Gomez 246

Alaska Quarterly Review

Vol. 39 No. 1 & 2   Winter & Spring 2023

Office Farewell Party	Carrie Shipers	248
A Poet Travels to the South	Brian Gyamfi	250
Compass	Susan Rich	252
Magnetic North	Jessica Tanck	253
Each Other Moment	Jessica Greenbaum	255
To My Ancestors	Brent Ameneyro	257
portal traveler	Allison Akootchook Warden.	258
When Home Says Stay	Sibongumusa Ncube	259
ancestry.com	John Bargowski	261
Father, Time	Stephen Ackerman	262
What Shines?	Sydney Lea	264
Portrait of Aphasia on a Plum Tree	Carolina Hotchandani	266
Memory	Kareem Tayyar	267
Hearts and Arrows	Hailey Leithauser	268
Hera, in Her 80s, Sorting Photographs	Constance Crawford	269
Love Is What This Is	Eva Saulitis	270

STORIES

ire'ne lara silva

song of the burning woman

Emma Elisa

I said I'd grow the flowers myself.

And I did. From seed. Now here they were, blooming everywhere, in every shade from lemon-yellow to gold to orange to dusky red. Solid and striped. Some the sizes of bushes. Others fit wholly in my hand with the roots lying on my wrist. Every variation I'd been able to find – African, French, Signet, Tangerine Scented, Spanish Tarragon, Irish Lace.

The idea came to me last year when I was taking down my Day of the Dead altar. I hadn't built such an elaborate one in decades. But the silence and the isolation had seemed to call for it. No one had thought we'd still be social distancing last November. I don't count the months anymore. I only remember it was a March when the world moved from one kind of time to another, one kind of space to another, one understanding of death to another.

---

ire'ne lara silva is the author of the collection of short stories *flesh to bone* (Aunt Lute Books, 2013). Her stories have appeared in *The Rumpus, Apogee, Pleiades, Blue Mesa Review, The Acentos Review,* and the *Nepantla Familias* anthology. She is the author of two chapbooks and four poetry collections, most recently *Cuicacalli/House of Song* (Saddle Road Press, 2019).

And the days and the months and the years were like an accordion, flexing this way and that, speeding up and then slowing down. People got sick. People got better. People died. It was a weird thing at first, to be a woman without family in a pandemic. I never knew my father. My mother died when I was in my twenties. No brothers, no sisters, no close cousins. No connections to elderly aunts or uncles. All those connections long gone. Left behind when I decided that neither hiding nor judgment were for me. I didn't know if they lived or died. Even before the pandemic, I'd sometimes search online for their names and add the word "obituary." As the years passed, there were fewer names to search.

I made my arrangements years ago. Before I retired. Went to the funeral home and laid everything out, paid for everything. My friend José said he'll deal with my art and Sol will take care of everything else. I'll leave no chaos behind me. Maybe my friends will gather, wish me well in the afterlife, pour a little tequila on the ground for me.

I've always loved parties. Loved the music and the colors and the people and their joy and the dancing and the food and the drinks. Loved the planning and the inviting and the way time ran swiftly at the start and then slowed syrup slow in the later hours. Loved those molten hours before dawn when only close friends remained and the brightness of the night glowed like an ember in my chest. I always loved my own parties best – because hosting kept me busy when melancholy threatened. Because if I needed to escape, I forgave myself the need to make excuses.

I used to love dancing. When I was young, I could dance for hours – flinging myself from one partner to another or dancing by myself or as part of a vast faceless crowd. I never cared if someone was watching – hell, sometimes I wanted everyone to watch. It never mattered to me as long as the beat compelled my body. When I grew older and one injury after another froze up my joints, the singing became everything. I'd sing until my voice turned to gravel, until it seemed my voice could fill the entire room, until everyone was singing with me, until I'd emptied out all the lyrics that lived in me. It didn't matter to me if I could sing or not, or if other people were off key, what mattered was that we sang together.

My house is a little house. Nothing special to anyone but me. Corner lot. Eight-foot wooden fence for the backyard that I put in for my ex because she used to lay out naked whenever the sun was shining.

Like a *pinche legartija* trying to get her cold-blooded heart pumping again. She left me three years ago. No fights. No arguments. She was just done with me. I finally got all her stuff out of the shed behind the house. I took anything someone could still use to the battered women's shelter. Tossed the rest of it. I didn't burn it like my dramatic heart wanted, but at least it's gone now. Next time she thinks to call or text me and promises to come pick it all up, I'll tell her, *Nah, don't worry about it. It's gone.* And she won't believe it. I know what she'll say. That I'm trying to make her hop on a plane and come see me. That I still want her back. She'll say it's because I never stopped loving her. That she knows she broke my heart and that I'll never be able to love anyone else again. But that's a lie. Only I know my capacity to love – and there's enough left for someone else. Enough love left for one more great love. Or maybe three little ones. Even though my hair's grey. Even though I've been retired for ten years. Even though my body is wrinkled and sagging and plump and scarred. But none of those things diminish me. I am more now than I have ever been.

It felt a bit odd to plan for a party again. I was cautious beyond cautious, waiting through pandemic waves. Years without drawing up lists and planning out the space and thinking of what I needed to build and who to invite. But even my cautious heart didn't want to wait anymore – it was time for a party. A small and lovely and long party. With talk and food and singing and dancing and art and photos. I asked Nora to make us *tacos* and Sol brought *pan dulce* and a huge pot of *caldo*. José volunteered to make drinks. I stocked up on *chorizo*, bacon, eggs, potatoes, and flour tortillas for whoever's still here at breakfast time. I cleaned and cleaned until not a speck of dust remained. I set up stations in the backyard – six large ones, seven small ones. Built them myself. They're not fancy – plywood and two-by-fours, hammered together with nails and prayers. And then I invited my friends to make altars of them.

I grew all the marigolds in anticipation of today. Marigolds along the fences and the house. Marigolds around the trees. Marigolds along the sidewalks. And marigolds bursting from My Lady. My Marigold Lady. Lady Cempasuchil. What else can I call her? She's a little bit of one thing, a little bit of another. Multi-hued marigolds bursting from her earthen flesh. A little Xochiquetzal, the goddess of flowers and art. A little bit of me. Somehow, she has my mother's eyes. I built her thirteen feet tall. You can feel her serene gaze from every corner of the backyard.

Pati

Ay, mira, it's been 29 years and she still builds an altar for me. That same photo in a silver frame. *Que bonito.* And my favorite peonies, without stems, on the lace tablecloth. The first time I held a peony in my hands I told Emma Elisa they reminded me of the plump bodies of doves. Soft, round, feathered. And look, a plateful of *tamales.* Chicken with *salsa verde,* each *tamal* tied with a little strip of corn husk. Like an extra blessing. Like little gifts. They're even still steaming. And a little shot glass with tequila. And a cup of my favorite coffee, that fancy coffee she would special-order for me that tasted like coconut.

I see the Big Flower Lady in the middle of the backyard. There's nowhere you can be that she can't see you. I like the *cempasuchil* but mostly I just see *chichis* and *nalgas* and flowers coming out of her whatchucallit – Emma Elisa says *yooohhhnis.* I used to ask her all the time why she made so many naked lady statues with breasts and *yooohhhnis* and she would say, *Ama, it's about a woman's eye seeing a woman. It's about the desires of women. Los deseos de mujeres.* And I would say, *Okay, but make me something else. I don't need woman parts on necklaces or earrings or keychains, m'ija. How about flowers? Or the sun and the moon?*

My poor Emma Elisa, all alone. Some years she has someone, but most years, she's alone. I wish I'd been able to give her some sisters and brothers. But she was my only. I didn't tell the doctors they could cut me, but they did. I was only nineteen. Went to the hospital alone. No insurance. The doctors said I was signing for painkillers. My mother said it was probably for the best, because I fell in love and I fell in love and I fell in love and none of them ever stayed. She said those lying doctors were a blessing in disguise, or I would have had twenty kids with twenty different fathers. She'd already raised me and my sisters. She said she didn't want to raise her grandchildren too. She never understood me – I just wanted somewhere to belong. I wanted someone to hold me and make me real. I wanted to make a home, a warm pretty place that didn't smell like bleach and fried potatoes. I wanted a man to put his arms around my shoulders, to put his hand on the small of my back, to keep me warm and weigh me down and fill me and exhaust me. I wanted a home filled with laughter and kisses and affectionate touches. The men came and went, came and went, but mostly it was just me and Emma Elisa.

So I filled our home with flowers and leafing things. Bought us a color TV and soft furniture that I never covered in plastic. Emma Elisa like to draw and make things so I bought her a few things every week – crayons, watercolors, construction paper, Play-Doh. I worked part-time as a cashier at a grocery store and picked up shifts at the Mexican restaurant a few blocks away. I tried not to leave Emma Elisa with my mother too often. She always came back too quiet and sometimes with tear tracks on her face. My best friend Mari had four kids and was a housewife, so mostly Emma Elisa ended up over there. When she got older, she helped care for the little ones, drawing them pictures and keeping them out of trouble. She was always independent. By the time she was twelve, she'd cook herself dinner and do her homework without my having to tell her anything.

When she was sixteen she told me she liked girls, not boys. I'd just woken up and was still wiping the sleep out of my eyes. She said it low, a little nervous, with a look in her eyes like she thought I might hit her or like she might cry. I'd never struck her or even spanked her because I never wanted to be like my mother. I pulled the blanket back and held my arms out to her. She made a little cry and I held her the way I'd held her when she was a little girl and afraid to sleep when there was thunder. I kissed her temple. *It's okay, m'ija, it's okay. You can love whoever you want to love.* And she cried, just a few tears, because my Emma Elisa was always strong like that. It took me a few minutes though before I thought to tell her that it would probably be best not to say anything to her grandmother.

I was dating Ruben then. I thought he was going to be the one. He stuck around for a while, but then he left too. And then there was Frankie. And Joel. Emma Elisa went to the community college for a couple years and then moved to Austin to go to UT. David used to take me up there to go see her every other month. Take us out to a nice dinner and to go see some of his buddies playing live music here and there. Before Emma Elisa graduated, she introduced me to her girlfriend Luisa and said she was following her back to San Francisco. By then, David was gone and I was seeing Michael. We flew out once to see Emma Elisa in California, and once she took the Greyhound to come spend a few weeks with me here.

And then I met Elias, and he really was the one. He got down on his knee to propose, and I wore his ring. We set a date and picked a cake and sent out invitations and even Mama liked him. But then that day came. We were going out for lunch, to that little *taqueria* we both liked so much on North 10th street with the *tacos de trompo* and the baked potatoes and the good lemonade. He was kissing my hand and I was looking at him and neither of us saw the truck that ran the red light.

We never got to promise each other till death do us part. But it was okay, because we'd already promised each other *forever, forever* and that's what it's been. Two years together in life, twenty-nine together in the afterlife. He's visiting his brother's family right now, but he'll be here before long. And he'll take my hand and bring it up to his lips to kiss it and he'll say my name and smile.

José

It's an art. I told Emma we weren't going to have that margarita mix shit from HEB. I brought all of my own bottles and ingredients. Enough Patron Silver to float us all away. My own syrups and fruit blends and garnishes. I had twenty-six specialties. One for every year Ismael and I were together. I didn't know it was going to become a tradition – that first year I invented El Mango Tango Wango Margarita and served it to him with *chorizo* and *papa taquitos* in bed while singing *"No Tengo Dinero"* at the top of my lungs. That went over so well the next year he got El Tierno Corazon de Melon Margarita with green salsa *chilaquiles* and *"Amor Eterno."*

The last time we celebrated an anniversary, he could barely eat or drink, but he sipped my Tulipan TinTan Te Quiero Mucho Margarita while I serenaded him with *"Yo No Vivo Por Vivir."* At the time, I didn't know how little time was left. The oncologist had estimated a few more months, but it was only a few weeks.

This is my first *Dia de los Muertos* without him. Elisa told me I could have one of the big *altares,* so I could do one of the big mixed media art and music installations I was known for. But that was "my work," and I didn't want to make anything that would be photographed and catalogued and written about. I didn't want to answer questions in the future about how important Ismael had been to me or what reaction grief transmuted into art should evoke in the viewer. I just wanted to remember Ismael. So I told her the kitchen counter would be all the altar I'd need.

Elisa had a ton of marigold bouquets and tall white candles all over the kitchen. I'd printed up a pretty little menu with all the drinks. And though they weren't expecting it, everybody got a little bit of a song with their drink: No Te Aguites Aguacate Margarita was served up with lyrics from *"El Noa Noa,"* the Cucurrucucu Coconut Margarita with *"Querida,"* and La Fresa Triste y Linda Margarita with *"La Diferencia."* That last one almost made me break into tears, but then again, *rancheras* are supposed to make you do that. So if my voice wobbled, it wasn't more than anyone expected.

I lost track of how many drinks I made, how many times the blender whirred, how many oranges, pineapples, strawberries, limes, mangos, and avocados moved through my hands. I spent my breaks eating the tiny little *tacos* Nora was making in the backyard with *fajitas, cebolla asada*, cilantro, and lime. I'd have a Corona and then go tour the altars as they were being built. I restrained myself mightily as I saw people struggling with color coordination and their arrangements. I reminded myself that love has its own aesthetic, that they would all look beautiful by the time they were done. If nothing else, we could always add more marigolds.

When Elisa wasn't looking in my direction, I'd grab a quick marigold bloom and eat it. When we first saw *Monsoon Wedding* years ago, it awoke a ferocious hunger in me for marigolds. I won't eat the ones from florists because I know they're full of chemicals, but I could never resist them when I saw the edible flower petals at the grocery store. Or when I saw them in people's yards. They taste a little smoky, a little spicy, a little bit like a single paint-stroke of sunlight on the tongue. /

There was a quiet hour, just as the sun was going down, when everyone was busy finishing the last details of their *altares*, laying down flowers and food and photos. And candles were being lit everywhere – twelve-day candles in multicolored glass, patron saints everywhere, the Virgen de Guadalupe and the Virgen de San Juan vastly outnumbering everything else. Elisa was everywhere, handing out little ceramic plates and saucers in an effort to cut down the risks of everything exploding and catching fire and burning her house down to the ground. I don't know what it was, but an impulse seized me and I took advantage of Mayra's arrival to uproot an entire bush of pretty striped marigolds that were growing in the backyard. Elisa never saw me since she was busy directing the lighting of the two-foot-tall beeswax candles Mayra had brought all around the Lady.

I plucked a pile of the deep green leaves and then pulled the petals free by the handful. I rinsed them and put them into two glass bowls with ice water. Under my breath I started singing and it took me a few lines to realize it was the chorus from Juanga's "*Siempre en mi Mente.*" Orange and grapefruit and lemon and lime and generous handfuls of marigold petals and this and that went into the blender. I was this close to pouring in some of the tequila when I suddenly thought of the three bottles of *mezcal* I'd brought to drink with Elisa and Kimberly. We always had *mezcal* when we were together, a tradition dating back to when we'd all been young artists in San Francisco. I'd brought three bottles of Del Maguey Vida Mezcal. I'd planned for us to drink one by morning and to gift them the other two, but I couldn't resist. Its smokiness would complement the marigolds like nothing else.

How to explain what happened with that first sip? The feeling I felt – like there was a small candle burning bright in my chest and its glow was growing and growing. I sang louder and louder and I didn't even know I knew all the words to the song. I thought of how much Ismael would have loved this gathering, how he would have taken up a spot close to the Lady and strummed his guitar, breaking into song throughout the whole night. How he would have come to the kitchen to see what I was making and then laugh when I'd catch him stealing my fruit garnishes. How he would have wrapped his arms around my waist and leaned in close to press a kiss behind my left ear. And I thought for a moment I could see his reflection in the kitchen window and feel his beard stubble on my neck. And I thought perhaps he hadn't really left me all alone. I salted the glasses and poured in the golden mixture and sipped it and for a moment tasted his lips again. And I sighed and named it – the Cempasuchil Siempre Margarita.

Nora

I brought Miguelito's favorite toys. His stuffed elephant that I'd named Don Policarpio and that he'd called Don Pio. A dozen little green army men, a jumble of Legos, his soccer ball. All the toys he hadn't been able to take with him when his grandfather took him.

I brought all the snacks he'd loved when he was little – a bag of Doritos, chocolate M&M's, the Mexican cookies with the pink and white puff marshmallows and coconut. Orange Fanta. I wasn't there to see what he kept on loving, what he outgrew, what new things became his favorite things. Every gift I ever gave him afterwards was a guess.

I had other things of his to add to the altar. His favorite jacket. His watch. The photo of a pretty dark-skinned girl that had been under his pillow. When everyone was at the funeral, I broke into the house and took these things. They were mine to take. Everything was mine – the scent of his pillow, the imprint of his feet in his shoes, the thick dark strands of hair in the comb on his nightstand.

And I took the framed photo my mother had of him in the living room.

I noticed every trace of me had been erased. Even after all this time I could see the darker places on the wood paneling where I remembered old family photos had hung. The photo of me and my two sisters on my tenth birthday. The photo of all of us that we'd taken at a special photography studio in Reynosa. My high school graduation photo. The photo of me in a high school football uniform. The photo of me at prom with Rosemary. All gone.

Back then, Rosemary had loved me as I was. It never mattered to her. I wore her clothes sometimes. She did my makeup and my hair. We did each other's pedicures and manicures. We'd kiss and taste Magenta Kiss/Red #578 on each other's mouths. We moved in together after high school and Miguelito came along before either of us turned twenty. My father wanted me to work with him, said I'd make more money in his shop than working as a waiter at Red Lobster. That one day I could take over the business. But I wasn't stupid enough to spend any more time than I had to around him. If it hadn't been for Rosemary, I wouldn't have survived my teen years at home. In his eyes, the only manly thing I'd ever done was make his first grandson.

I worked all the time those first years. So I don't know when it started. Better said, I don't know when it started to get worse. Rosemary had always liked to party. She'd keep on drinking as long as there was something to drink. Would smoke or swallow or sniff anything anyone gave her. She cut down a lot when we moved in together. I think it was because we were both free of our families for the first time. And then she got pregnant. We were so happy. She worked a part-time job and spent that money on a crib and toys. When Miguelito was born, she stayed at home with him. Maybe that's when it started. But it wasn't until he was three that I'd come home after a double shift and find Miguelito eating a pile of Lucky Charms on the floor and Rosemary passed out on the couch. Beer bottles everywhere and the stench of pot in the air.

I started seeing some of our old friends from high school coming back around again. And all the signs were there. She was doing coke again. Taking whatever anyone gave her. We started fighting all the time.

At the same time, my mom kept calling and asking me to come by with Miguelito. Said it wasn't enough to see their only grandson on holidays and their birthdays. But it was just so hard every time we went there. Everyone at work and in our neighborhood knew me as Nora. Miguelito called Rosemary, "Mommy," and me, "Mama." He was too little to understand that everything had to be different at my parents' house. And it wasn't like I could just wash my face and strip the nail polish off – I had to drill all these reminders into my head for days before every visit – how to walk, how to talk, what to say, what not to say, how to say it, how not to say it, to mirror my father's mannerisms, to take up space, to not show too much affection, to not take my plates to the sink, to say that Rosemary wasn't feeling well, to say that no, my mom and my sisters didn't need to come check on her or cook for me or watch Miguelito, that the drive from Los Fresnos was too far. And every time I left their house, I'd drive to the grocery store parking lot close to Business 83 and just bury my face in my arms and cry and cry with relief to have made it through. And Miguelito would cry with me.

My friend Ani stopped waitressing when she had her baby. She started watching Miguelito for me.

Rosemary and I kept fighting. And then she ended up in jail after she got pulled over when she was high. I got home one day after I picked up Miguelito, and all her stuff was gone. Things went to hell quickly after that. My parents heard from Rosemary's parents that she'd left. They came looking for me at work. Instead of Miguel Jr., they found Nora. They reported me to CPS for child abuse. They sued for custody. The judge called me a deviant in court.

I couldn't find an attorney who would take my case. I tried filing the paperwork on my own, but the judge had me declared a vexatious litigant after denying me custody and then visitation. My father threatened to shoot me if he saw me. My parents adopted Miguelito and had my name taken off his birth certificate.

No Miguelito. No Rosemary. No family.

I still tried to make a life, to be true to myself. I was Nora and never had to pretend to be Miguel Jr. again. I left Red Lobster and opened up a taco truck. After a while, added a few tables, then a jukebox, cement to make a dance floor, a ceiling to shield people from the sun and the rain. Got a liquor license and sold beer.

I fell in love a few times. I had friends.

None of them knew I was also a ghost. That I watched my son from afar. Watched him go to school and run around outside during recess. Wondered if he cried for me before he fell asleep. Watched him as he grew taller and taller. Wondered if he remembered me at all.

And the years passed, and I had a little hope. That maybe when he was 18 and living on his own, I would walk up to his door and hold him again.

But I never did. An aneurysm took him when he was in high school. Even when he was dead, they wouldn't let me hold him.

Mike

Death's messed up. It's all these little flashes of lights. And memories. 'Buelo said he'd shoot him if he came around. But I just wanted to know him. Well, her, I guess. My dad. My mom. Whatever. They told me he was crazy and he'd hurt me if I went with him. It messed with my head. I saw him . . . her . . . everywhere I went. Sometimes during recess when I was a kid, she'd be parked in a car on the street next to the playground. When we'd go to the *pulga* or the HEB, she'd be following us, staying out of 'Buela's sight. I'd see her at church, six pews away, black lace over her face. But I always knew it was her. I didn't know if she wanted to steal me away or what. And even though my 'Buelo said his son was a pervert and a sin against God, I didn't get mad when I saw her. She made me sad. I thought about all my friends who didn't have their fathers no more, and I thought at least mine wanted me.

She'd leave little gifts for me in the mailbox on Saturdays. Small things nobody would notice. A little Hot Wheels car, a sack of marbles, some M&M's. When I got older, she'd leave a rolled up five-dollar bill, then tens, then twenties.

'Buelo and 'Buela were strict when I was little. I went to school, came home, did chores, did homework. Weekends went to more chores and church and big meals with all my uncles and aunts and cousins. The older I got, the more I looked like 'Buelo, and as long as I did what my 'Buelo wanted, I got to do what I wanted and go where I wanted. I got a driver's license and my 'Buelo's barely used Ford F-150 as soon as I turned 15. When 'Buela said I should be getting home before midnight, 'Buelo told her it was *"cosas de hombre"* and she needed to let me become a man, so I wouldn't turn out like the *desgraciado* her son was.

None of my friends had chores to do. And there were always parties to go to. Somebody's parents would be gone. There was an empty lot behind the abandoned gas station where we'd drink and hang out with our girls. I got into a few fights sometimes, but nothing worse than a black eye or a few bruises. 'Buelo would only laugh and clap me on the shoulder the few times I came home a little drunk or a little bruised. He'd say, *See, he can handle his liquor and drive himself home fine*, or, *See, this one don't get beat down!*

I don't remember what my mom looked like. Or what her voice sounded like. Or how she smelled. But I remember crying and crying for my Mama. And how confused 'Buelo and 'Buela were because they kept telling me she'd left a long time ago. They threw away every photo that had either of my parents in it. Their names weren't even on the birth certificate 'Buela kept in a zipped-up bank bag with her important papers. My mom never came to look for me, never called, never wrote, but I saw my Mama everywhere.

I didn't make the best grades in high school, and I wasn't on the football team or anything, but I had lots of friends and I never went more than a couple of days without a girlfriend after I turned 12. Lost my virginity when I was 13. I never got anyone pregnant cuz I was careful. I'd heard too many times how my idiot father had gotten my whore of a mother pregnant and that if I hadn't looked so much like him, my 'Buelo would have wondered if I was even his grandson.

I liked having girlfriends. I like messing around with them, but none of them ever really made me feel anything. If one of 'em broke up with me, there was always another one waiting. And if I saw a girl I liked more than the one I had, then I'd break up with one and go around with the other.

Until I met Araceli. 'Buelo didn't like her. He said she was too dark. That I was a good-looking kid and I could marry White or at least one of those *rubias*, all blonde and blue-eyed even though their last names were Garcia or Gonzalez or Reyna. But I thought she was the most beautiful girl I'd ever seen. She had the most beautiful eyes, a little slanted and a hot gold color. Her skin was dark and beautiful, so clear and smooth. She was so funny and a little bit of a smartass in class. She was always having to stay late for detention for talking back to the teachers, so I'd wait for her in the parking lot until they let her out. What I loved most about her, though, was that she was so *cariñosa*. None of my girlfriends had ever touched me like that. Most of them would put their hands on me like they wanted to show that they owned me. Or they'd wrap my arm around their shoulders or their waists like they wanted all my attention all the time. But Araceli would touch me softly, her hand on my arm or my shoulder, for just a moment. If I pulled her even slightly towards me, she'd cuddle into my side or sit on my lap. Without any shyness, she'd press little kisses next to my eyes, on my jaw, sometimes even on my hands. She'd run her fingers through my hair or drum the beat of whatever song was playing in her head on my chest.

The first time we were together, everything was so slow. There was no rush but no hesitation. The afternoon light was streaming in through the window. I kissed her eyes. I cupped her small breasts and marveled over her dark nipples. I memorized the scent of her. The color of her sex like the *amaranto* that grew in our backyard. When she kissed me, she held my face with both hands. And even after we both came, her legs and arms were still tight around me.

She became my whole world. I told 'Buelo I was going to marry her. He called her horrible names and said I was too stupid to know what I was doing. That he'd given me everything I had and that he could take it all back. I told him that if he couldn't respect her, I'd walk right out the door. He could have his pickup back. He could find someone else to leave his auto body shop to. That I'd walk out the door naked if I had to.

Next thing I knew there was a bright light and a red wash of blood and then I was gone. I saw 'Buelo's shocked face for a split second.

I didn't take anything when I left my grandparents' house. Not even my body.

Araceli cried and cried for me. I pressed kisses against her eyes. I hope she felt them.

Sol

I asked if I could have one of the small *altares*. Elisa didn't laugh at me when I told her I wanted to make one for my little Luz.

Guillermo never wanted us to have a dog, so as soon as we split up, I went straight to the shelter. Luz didn't have a name yet. He was one of five puppies that had been brought in a few days before. He was puppy #3. It was love at first sight. He was sleepy and looked like a grumpy old man. A pretty golden color all over with the blackest eyes and nose. A white splash on his chest and neck. *Luz de mi vida*, I thought, he was going to be the light of my life.

And I needed a puppy's uncomplicated and pure love. Needed to take care of him and make a home for us both.

I barely knew who I was after the wreck of my nineteen-year marriage. Guillermo and I had only tolerated each other for years, but we probably would have stayed together and just lived miserable if it hadn't been for Estella. For the longest time I told myself I was just imagining things. That Estella was just coming by the *panadería* almost every morning because she just liked our coffee and *pan dulce*. Told myself she just wanted to be friends. We'd meet for *tacos*. We'd go out for drinks. We'd catch a movie together. Guillermo was glad I'd made a friend, said it gave him a chance to go hang out with his buddies without my always checking on him. Estella was fun and we had so much in common. And I told myself we were just good friends. Until I found myself with my tongue down her throat and her fingers inside me.

And I got careless or maybe I wanted Guillermo to know.

It'd been going on for several months before he came home unexpectedly, and there we were in the living room, my head between her legs.

He wasn't even angry. We didn't even argue. He just packed his stuff and left. We met with his attorney. I got the house, and he took everything in our accounts. Estella didn't last very long. I didn't have a lot of time for her. Within the year, my mom got really sick, and I took care of her until she died. My dad only lasted a few weeks after her funeral. Doctor said natural causes, no issues, he just passed away in his sleep. And I wondered what that would be like, to be loved so much your husband couldn't live without you. They left the *panadería* to me. My brother got their house and the couple acres it came with.

Little Luz was there for all my grief, for all my loneliness, for all the time afterwards. He was there as I dated woman after woman and they broke my heart. I don't think I've ever known what I was looking for. I just know I never found it.

Luz would come with me to the bakery. He became the unofficial mascot. He wasn't allowed into the kitchen, of course, but he had free run of the little area where we had a couple booths for people to sit and eat at. Business was good and over the years, I started expanding. I changed the name of the *panadería* from *Reyna's Panadería* to *Mi Luz Panadería*. The new sign and all our boxes and bags bore the new logo – a half sun with little Luz's face.

Business was good. We made all the traditional *pan dulce* the way my parents had taught me: *molletes* – called *conchas* everywhere else – *hornitos*, pink cake, *donas* – Mexican donuts were not American donuts – *marranitos*, *pan de polvo* with cinnamon and sugar, *pan de polvo* with powdered sugar, strawberry jelly rolls, *mantecados*, *churros de cajeta, orejas,* tri-colored cookies, *empanadas de camote* and *calabaza* and *piña* and *manzana*, all in all enough *pan dulce* to fill the six-foot cases. I decided to add *tacos* to the menu. Added *caldo* and *menudo* on the weekend mornings. I poured every cent of profit back into the *panadería*. I knocked down one wall and expanded the kitchen and the seating area. More of the college kids started coming around along with families and the old retired men that needed somewhere to meet up for a few hours every day. I bought an espresso machine the same day I put in Wi-Fi. We went from closing at 3pm to 5pm to 7pm to 9pm.

I met Elisa when she came in to order *pan dulce* for a reception she was hosting for a friend. I'd never known an artist before and never one that wanted 200 mini *marranitos* and 200 mini *molletes* and 500 heart-shaped *pan de polvo* cookies. While we were talking, she ended up trying some of our *caldo de pollo* with shredded chicken and *calabazitas* and potato and rice and carrots and tomatoes and cilantro and lime juice, and before I knew it, she'd ordered enough *caldo* for a hundred people.

When I was directing the delivery and set up at the reception, Elisa brought me a glass of wine. I mentioned that it had been the favorite wine of an ex. She tilted her head at me for a second and said her ex had taught her to love it. *Nereida,* we both said at the same time. I laughed and said it made us like in-laws of in-laws, that it was too bad there was no word for the ex of an ex. In a low and dramatic voice she said, *the ex of my ex is my friend,* and then clasped both my hands with hers.

Elisa was the one I called when the veterinarian told me it'd be best to let Luz go. That the cancer was just too advanced and that the pain was too much for his little body.

He was with me for longer than my marriage lasted. Twenty years of his big eyes and his furry little face. Twenty years of cuddles and walks. I took him almost everywhere with me. During the hot months, I carried him, only allowing his little paws to touch grass and earth. I would think sometimes about that little rhyme, *ni madre ni padre ni perro que me ladre,* but it was never true for me. Because even though I was otherwise alone in the world – no mother, no father, no husband, no children, sometimes no girlfriend – I always had little Luz.

Until now. So I brought his favorite little sun-and-moon-shaped bacon treats. His favorite toy, Mr. Bebop, the little pig that squeaked when he'd carry him in his jaws, and Shushu, the rainbow glow-worm he wouldn't sleep without. I had a thousand different photos of Luz. It took hours to choose my favorites. The base of the altar was his last dog bed and his favorite pillow. I made paper flowers to string everywhere. The last thing I added to the altar was his leash and his collar with the metal tag with his name.

My little Luz.

Feliciana
I don't think this is the right house. I don't know any of these people. I was passing by on the other side of street and saw a young woman I thought was my granddaughter. Her hair is just like hers. Black black and falling straight past her hips. She was carrying yards and yards of fabric in her arms. All colors, *bien vivos.* Lots of yellow and orange and turquoise and green. And then a bag from the *mercado,* all full of ribbons and lace and spools of thread.

Before the arthritis in my hands got too bad, I used to spend my days making blankets. I'd sell them at the Bargain Bazaar. I made a lot of baby blankets. Those were very popular, because they didn't cost as much as the queen- or king-size ones. When people would complain my blankets cost too much, I'd tell them, *If you want a cheap blanket, go to WalMart. You won't find any blankets like these there. This is good fabric, everything sewn by hand, even the ruffle edging. I bought the softest, thickest cotton batting, and feel here, I layered it and stitched it into place. This blanket will last you the rest of your life – you'll be able to pass it on to your children!*

No, this girl's not my granddaughter. She looks so serious! My *nieta* was always laughing. But I hear music and voices. *Bien alegre.* And there are people singing. I want to go listen. They won't notice me. I won't make too much noise. I'll just find somewhere to sit. And someone's making *tacos* – I can smell corn tortillas on the *comal*! O some *bistec* with *cebollitas asadas* and a squeeze of lime would be so delicious!

Yes, there's a little comfy chair in this corner, under the tree, where the breeze is just right. And a young man, so polite, very gentlemanly, just brought me a glass of *agua de jamaica* with a little bit of ice, just like I like it. He says he'll bring me the next plate of *tacos*.

Que bonito. There's a lot of people here. I don't know any of them. There are kids playing and running around with a little dog. There are so many flowers. I've never seen so many marigolds at the same time in my life! Then there are people gathered around the woman making *tacos*, waiting their turn and singing. And all these tables with photos and food and flowers and candles.

I don't think any of those are for me, but no one's telling me I don't belong. *Aquí me quedo.*

This house must belong to that woman right there. Every person that comes in hugs her first. And she keeps pointing in one direction and then another. She's wearing a man's shirt that's too big on her and the bottom of her pants are ragged – she cut them but never hemmed them. I could take care of both those things in just a few minutes. That's how I brought in money when my children were little. Alterations. I'd fix everything – men's suits, missing buttons, sleeve lengths, pants, church dresses, wedding gowns, *quinceañera* dresses, uniforms. So many uniforms – maids, cooks, nurses, mailmen, school uniforms – everything!

How nice! The young man didn't forget me – he brought me a plate with two *tacos de bistec* with cilantro and grilled onion and radish slices and lime wedges. Even two rolled-up napkins.

I can't stop looking at The Lady. She's so beautiful. Her face peaceful, round but with strong cheekbones. Intelligent eyes. The clay of her is dark, dark. And now that the sun is setting, all the marigolds in her arms and bursting from her body make it look like she's on fire.

She reminds me of Chela. Chela had eyes like that. Like she was always thinking. And when I'd ask her what she was thinking, she'd always make me either laugh or cry. I miss her so much. Our husbands were best friends all their lives. My mother died when I was young. My sisters were all much older than me. I'd never had a best friend until I met Chela. Roberto introduced me to her and Eligio the first time we went to the Saturday night dance at the church hall. I was seventeen. Chela was eighteen. She and Eligio had already been married for two years and had a baby boy.

I loved her so much. We took care of each other's children. We cooked for each other's families. We spent many holidays and birthdays together. At first, we only hugged, sometimes we sat and held each other's hands. It wasn't until after all our children had grown and moved away that she pulled me towards her and kissed me. And I kissed her back. It was nothing like kissing Roberto. I loved my husband, but when Chela touched me, it was like finally, everything was right and nothing was missing. We stayed with our husbands until they died but spent as much time together as we could.

Roberto died first, a heart attack when he was sixty-six. Then Eligio when he was seventy-four. Cancer. Chela and I moved in together. None of our children thought it was odd. It only made sense for two *viejitas* who were best friends to share a house. I never thought I would be the happiest I ever was in my life in my sixties. Every night, Chela slept in my arms. Every morning, her voice was the first sound I heard. And what a thrill I felt, every time I ran my hand down along her naked hip. After so many decades of longing, neither of us cared that our hair had gone grey, our flesh rounded and our skin loose, our joints sometimes stiff. What mattered was that we were free to reach for each other.

Now I'm just waiting for her. She comes from long-lived people. She must be in her nineties already.

I've been looking for her all day. She's not in the house we lived in. She's not in any of her children's houses. I'm not sure if it's been ten years or twenty already since I died. I was starting to forget things while I was still alive. But not Chela. Never Chela. I'm going to finish these delicious *taquitos*. Then I'll get my things and keep on looking. I can hear her voice calling my name. And my heart was always a lit flame for her, my love spilling out of me like all the marigolds spilling out of The Lady's arms.

Xochitl

I still can't get used to calling her Elisa. I keep calling her Profe. She says that's not right. I tell her, you teach a class at the university, we get to call you Profe. It just seems disrespectful to call her Elisa or Mssss!

I don't feel like I know what I'm doing here. No matter what I do, it's just not right. And it's not enough. Profe says my hope has to be bigger than my despair. That I need to transform all this rage into love. But I don't know how to do either of those things.

Most of the time art feels totally useless. Here I am, making this huge altar dedicated to lives lost crossing the border, to all the children lost at residential schools, to murdered and missing Indigenous women, to the Ayotzinapa 43, to the Latin American environmental activists that have been killed. And there's news clippings and names and photos and all my *ofrendas* and I've laid it all out like I'd sketched it out for Profe to take a look at.

But now that it's all here, it feels like it's nothing. It's just here, in Profe's backyard for as long as this party lasts. Tomorrow, we'll be taking it all down. Sure, she says that we'll document it while it's up. That it can be shared online. That I'll have all the materials to do an installation anywhere in the future. And she says she's going to introduce me to José Camargo – her friend, she says, her friend – like he's not super famous. We studied his work in one of my classes. My professor literally cried when he told us about the first time he saw José Camargo's work in person.

My altar doesn't *feel* like anything. It just looks like pieces, like a kid's collage. It doesn't come together. It's not one thing. It doesn't build, it doesn't feel natural or inevitable or forceful or anything. It doesn't *coalesce*, like Profe says. It doesn't have any *moments*.

She told me about an installation she saw when she was in college. Amalia Mesa Bains' *Vanidades*. How it had moments where everything paused for her. How she felt alone and immersed even though she was in a gallery with other people. How much she wanted to touch the hair brush on the vanity. How in that space she might as well have been smelling her mother's talcum powder and body soap. How the world shifted when she looked at her own face in the mirror and saw Cesar Chavez' face superimposed over hers.

I've only ever made one thing that I felt really worked. It was the project I submitted at the end of my semester with Profe. Mixed media. Part earth, part fabric, partly painted, partly embroidered. A tribute to my parents. They were both musicians, gunned down by drug dealers in some no-name bar in a small town. I was sent to live with my Aunt Rosie in Utah. I was only four. She and my Uncle Bob changed my name from Xochitl to Danielle and never spoke to me in Spanish.

They couldn't understand why I'd choose to apply to a university in South Texas. Why I'd go back to where my parents had come from. I applied and got a full scholarship. During my freshman year I drove the couple miles from the university to the courthouse and changed my name back to Xochitl. I let the blonde highlights and the coloring Aunt Rosie had insisted on grow out. I walked in the sun as much as I wanted to and watched my skin darken. I took three years of Spanish and listened to Tejano on the radio station and watched telenovelas on the Mexican TV channels until I could understand what people were saying.

I'd only ever seen my grandparents once a year when I lived in Utah. I started to spend time with them and my aunts and uncles and cousins. I started to visit my parents in the cemetery. It was in the cemetery that I knew what I wanted to do for my final project for Profe. I sat there on the ground, a bit dazed, as image after image bloomed in my mind. And then I raced home to begin. I'd never worked so hard on anything before. Never spent just hours and hours sitting with it and tracing parts of it with my fingertips and dreaming about it and talking to it. And it would tell me what else was missing. And then there was a morning when I looked at it and it was just *alive*. And I knew I was done.

Emma Elisa

I don't know what made me start but once I started I knew I would never stop. It started with small drawings, with crayons and clay and watercolors. I never knew we were poor because there was always food and there was always paper and crayons and paints and clay. Mama never said anything if I used all the aluminum foil or if I cut up our towels or if I painted on the walls. Almost every day when she came to pick me up after work, she'd bring me something. Not dolls or dresses but construction paper and glue and pipecleaners and glitter.

As I got older, she bought me pencil sets and charcoals, canvases and acrylics, pastels and self-hardening clay. There was a year I picked up cross stitch and needlepoint and knitting. I had plastic bins stacked five feet tall with all my supplies and all my projects. Mama never fussed when I brought in twigs, leaves, wildflower bouquets, clumps of earth, rocks, mesquite bean pods, or bits of fallen nests.

Which is sort of what my house looks like now that I've lived in it alone since *La Legartija* left. What was a three-bedroom house no longer even has a dedicated guest room. There's my bedroom which is also partly a studio, the second bedroom which has always been my studio, and the used-to-be guest room which has a bed hidden somewhere under my current projects. The kitchen is mostly clear, except for the breakfast nook which now has my easel and several canvases. The living room has several towers of books I'm planning to start reading, but there's enough room for at least eight people to sit. And the dining room's free now too. I think I threw everything I had on the dining table and the chairs in the pantry. I'll bring it all back out after the party.

I told everybody they can party and drink all they want, but there's nowhere to sleep except on the floor or in the backyard, where they're free to lay out a blanket or a serape or a sleeping bag. I left out a small pile on the patio along with some old throw pillows in case anyone gets tired.

I want to do this the way Mama used to tell me she remembered it. Spend all day preparing and laying out the altars, stay up all night holding vigil, break bread all together in the morning.

Of course, my friends started drinking the moment they got here. Dusk is falling now. Most of the *altares* are done. Just a few people still scrambling now with finishing touches. So glad Nora came. She's been making the most amazing *tacos* all day. I wasn't sure if she was going to be all right. We've been friends for a decade, even dated for a little while, but I'd never known she had a son until she found out he'd died. I kept my distance while she was working on her son's altar. There was a moment there where it seemed like she was flinging marigold petals at it. I could almost see the flowers bleeding in her hands as she twisted the petals off.

José's been a sweetheart with the drinks. I'm so glad he's here too. His first *Dia de los Muertos* without Ismael. I caught him singing earlier while he was handing out drinks. It'd been a while since I'd heard him singing. The world's not right if he's not singing or humming under his breath. He thinks I haven't noticed he's been stuffing his face with my marigolds. If he'd asked, I would have told him to eat as many as he wanted. I'm not saving them for anything. I grew them for today.

I'm glad Antonio's here. He says his wife will come by tonight after she gets out of the hospital. He hasn't said anything but I think he's a little nervous about how his wife will react to the altar he created. It's so beautiful – it has a marvelous stillness and reverence and simplicity. Photos of his mother, his brother, his first love, and the child that was never born. White roses and sunflowers and red roses and pink and red hibiscuses. And all these gorgeous origami birds. I met Antonio at one of my favorite *taquerias*. I usually go at least twice a week after the lunch rush, but I went there early one day since I'd skipped breakfast. The place wasn't busy, and we must have been at least ten feet away from each other. I was busy sketching some new ideas and must have forgotten where I was since I started singing along with the music playing on the jukebox. One of my favorite old songs from an LP my mother had inherited from her father.

I didn't realize I was singing along until Antonio decided to join in too. I looked up in surprise. *I love Los Cadetes de Linares too,* he said with the widest smile. Just like that, we were friends. Before long, he told me his story. And I told him there was nothing better than art to pour your life and your stories and your pain and your love into. So he's been trying out new things, reading me poems or stories, showing me sketches, researching different artists I tell him about and trying out different things. This is the first time he's come over to my house. His eyes looked so large as I gave him an impromptu tour through all my messy art rooms.

Xochitl came with us too. She kept apologizing every time she reached out to touch some half-formed thing. I laughed and told her none of it would break, and if it did break, there wasn't anything I couldn't fix. I didn't know when I took on the task of teaching a class at the university that I was going to end up loving all of my students. Xochitl, though, I can feel it – I'm going to know her for the rest of my life. You can practically feel the insatiable drive to learn, to create, to make sense of it all radiating off of her. She's hard on herself, but it makes her exacting and the kind of stubborn you have to be to make art.

A couple years before I turned fifty everything changed for me. Decades of different cities, with different partners and helping to raise their children for a few years here and there, while working one IT job with health insurance after another. Mind-numbing forty-hour work weeks interrupted by a show on the East Coast, in London, in Paris, and then back to the eight-to-five. Impossible to describe what it took to split myself between the work that paid the bills and my real work for so many decades. As the years passed, my hands learned to follow what my imagination dreamed, learned to translate what my heart felt into something I could touch.

And then I heard something on the wind. And with a sudden ferocity, I wanted to come back to the Valley, to the border, to the Gulf, to the place where I grew up. I wanted the food I grew up with and the music I grew up with. I wanted to live on a palm tree-lined street and for my bougainvillea to climb my mesquite trees and spill color everywhere. I wanted a little home like this one and a life like this one and friends like these. This is where I want to live all the years I have left. In my messy house full of half-finished art. Dreaming things and making things.

Like my Lady Cempasuchil. Her face implacable and joyful. The curve of a generous hip and then a muscled thigh, a rounded shoulder and then a strong forearm. Absence and presence. All these hollow spaces within her to fill with earth, to fill with seed, to offer up to the sunlight.

She's been complete for a week now. What I dreamed and what blossomed all coming together. Aflame.

It looks like Sol is finished with her altar for little Luz. She's holding one of his toys in her hands, an unbearable sadness on her face. I'm going to go see if I can get Carlos to play some *Angeles Azules*. Sol's never been able to resist a *cumbia*. I'll see if I can pull her away to dance with me, bare feet on the grass, just so I can see her eyes light up again.

The Lady
She made me with her hands. Her hands both cool and molten. She dreamed me, she molded me, she smoothed shaped and named me. She whispered me, she sang me, she screamed muttered growled me. She called invited invoked me.

So I came. And I calmed the winds. And I calmed the border blood. I came here, to her home, modest material and human but concentrated with power as if lightning slept in it.

I have been cradling this earth and murmuring to these little blossoms. They are mine and I am theirs. And on this night of ancestors I will keep the peace. For the voices that weep for the spirits flickering through. Enter. You are welcome. But you cannot stay. Lightning lives here.

I will come and go. Blossom and burn. Sing and bloom. Bloom and bloom.

Live and live and live until the day comes when this body will fall to the ground with a thud, and lay there, collapsed like a pile of rocks.

Kate Blakinger

NEVER SPEAK THE WORD DROWN

Larsen met her at Shakey's, where the bar girls wore number tags pinned to their dresses so a man could remember who was "his girl." Number Eleven sat apart at the bar, paying no attention to anyone, blades of her shoulders stretching the fabric of her blue dress, waxy red lipstick on her frowning mouth. A band played Elvis covers on a rickety stage not ten feet from her, but she remained self-contained, indifferent to the music, as if saturated with secret thoughts. The other girls, circled by the entrance, trying hard to entice, interested Larsen less.

He ordered a beer, and a cocktail for her. Ignoring his chit-chat, she leaned over and plucked an egg out of a covered basket that sat on the counter. She rapped the egg against the edge of the bar and cracked it open. Eyes on him, she sipped liquid from the bottom of the shell, then spilled the rest of its contents into her palm: a baby duck, feathers half-formed, a blind eye like a drop of licorice, tiny

Kate Blakinger's stories have appeared in *Epiphany*, *The Iowa Review*, *Gettysburg Review*, and *New Stories from the Midwest*.

twig feet, whole thing wet and glistening. This was a surprise, and it shut Larsen up. She shook salt over the abomination curled in her hand, lifted it to her mouth and bit it in half. His stomach clenched.

She leaned toward him, face lively, watchful, and she offered him the rest. "You want to try *balut*?" she said.

He fingered the blob tentatively, shoved it in his mouth. The taste was savory, not terrible, but the texture undid him, the wetness, the feel of feathers and feet on his tongue. He tried to make his jaw work. He was sweating. The guys at the nearest table hooted at him as he lifted his San Miguel and gulped sloppily. He drained the bottle, and somehow, by some shred of grace, he swallowed the dead duck.

The girl's name was Tala. He found she lived all in one room, a little refrigerator and hot pot on one side, her bed along the opposite wall. The floor was cement, the walls unpainted wood – a modest place but not one of the shanties that piled up along Olongapo's back alleys.

As she squatted before Larsen and ran her scissors across his yellowed toenails, it occurred to him maybe he was putting her through something more intimate than sex. His toes were in a state of grotesque neglect. The nails dirty and jagged, his feet pale and stinking. She didn't seem fazed. When she finished, he asked if she'd also cut his hair. She lifted the scissors. Every tension he held in his body fell away with the hair she removed. He listened to the creak and snip as the blades closed and cut and bits of hair fell free to the floor.

He touched the crown of his head, feeling the change. It was late, and she was likely tired, but still she smiled at him as she swept hair from the floor.

Larsen's wife, Josie, said it was a small tyranny the way men were always wanting women to smile upon them. Josie would no longer smile, or tolerate his touch, or touch him, not since their son had died then been born, face grey-blue as a storm cloud, cord around his neck.

Tala set the broom aside. She lifted her dress over her head. Larsen felt his wife looking at him through the shack's tiny window. This was impossible – 7,000 miles of ocean separated San Francisco and Olongapo City – but still he couldn't shake the vision of Josie spying through the glass. Fumbling, sorrowful, he made for the door at once, leaving a pile of cash behind on the bed, alarmed at himself, for it was damning to be here, enclosed in this room with a naked woman, noticing, in flashes, her breasts, the softness of her stomach, the dark hair at her groin. She wore no undergarments. All this time, she'd been practically naked, and now he would never be able to forget.

* * *

Tala was glad the same American chose her again the next night. She wasn't the most beautiful. She wasn't the youngest. What the men wanted was someone who drew them out, who listened, a woman whose touch and attention made them feel the exact shape of their lives mattered.

He told her he wasn't stationed at the American naval base, wasn't fighting in Vietnam. He'd come to the Philippines from Saigon, though. The war was where merchant mariners ended up, their ships winding up the Saigon River, shuttling supplies in, hauling away the army's trash.

Haircuts were easy, but still, Tala was relieved to coax him into bed. It would mean more money. He folded the clothes he removed and piled them neatly. He lay beside her. In a hoarse, half-whisper brushing at her ear, he confessed he had a wife.

"But you're so young," she said. "No ring."

He laughed, flattered, said he wasn't that young.

As the American pressed into her, she lay still and she left, her body pinned against the lumpy mattress, her mind lifting. A vexed and tender warmth billowed in her chest as she thought of Vito telling her a boastful story, veering into make-believe, his childish voice leaping, his dark, gleaming eyes staring at her even as he sprung about the room, pausing his motion only to give her a serious look, lips a tight line, stubborn chin warding off disbelief. When he was with her, stories crowded his mouth. Capers, tricks he'd played on soldiers. Quick escapes, rides hitched on Jeepneys, dodging the mayor's thugs. He was only eight or nine, small, carved and bony – but he was lit with vitality, and people leaned close when he spoke.

She sank back into her body. In the sweaty afterward, the American held her. His face, buried in her hair, grew wet. Crying sailors were nothing rare. She soothed the American, stroking his back, somehow stirred to sympathy, yet at the same time repulsed, resentful, turned to ice. She pretended to care, and then she did, but only a little.

Sweat still lay wet on their bodies when Vito entered without warning. Tala made a sound of surprise. The child knew which nights not to come. Yet, here he was, and the skin around his right eye was purple, swollen tight over his eyeball like a closed mouth, eyebrow above flecked with crumbs of dried blood. The American pushed out of bed, began putting on clothes.

She yanked on her dress, touched Vito gently on the small of his back. He wore no shirt. "You must run faster, Vito. What happened

33

to the lightning in your legs?" Whenever large foreign ships docked, the mayor's men captured the street children and locked them out of sight in the jail. If Vito was caught, she wouldn't see him for days. He'd return crawling with lice. Raw sores from sleeping on damp stone floors would ooze on his back.

"Who did this? Same men as last time?" she asked.

"There were three of them. Thought they had me."

"You got free."

"All they got was my shirt," he said, flashing her an amused look, then wincing. Tala could picture Vito twisting deftly free of his shirt. He wanted her to laugh, but she couldn't. Looking at his mashed face, anger squeezed out every other feeling.

The American eased his feet into battered shoes. "Your son?" he asked. With his golden skin and loose curls, Vito did not resemble Tala. She'd given birth to a boy who would be about his age, but her baby had been taken from her, and now she looked out for Vito, gave him her mothering.

"This is Vito."

"What happened?" the American asked.

"Please. You need to leave." She dabbed Vito's torn skin with iodine, helping his body heal. She wanted to do more, guard whatever fire still shimmered inside him. "We could ice that eye," the American said. "I have aspirin. I could get some."

"What does he want?" Vito asked her in Tagalog.

"To help, he says."

She thought of that wife, across an ocean somewhere, in a house with many rooms. Married to this man, this American who carried himself with an easy swagger, in the bar, in the streets, in Tala's home. He waded into the world, and the world made room, accommodating him easily as a warm bath. His eyes were pale, like the edges of the sky where the blue fades, easing into smoke and haze. Too pale to show his soul. His nose had been whittled to crooked angles, cheeks stubbled over, hair a dusty brown and neatly cropped now along his creased forehead, sadness imprinted lightly around his eyes.

"If you want to help," she said slowly, "you could hide us."

"Hide you." A bemused disbelief colored his voice.

"Take us with you in your ship."

"Nowhere safe to hide on a ship. People crawl into the damned bilges in the engine room. If we didn't fish them out, they'd drown."

"You see what happens here. He's a child."

"You need a man who can marry you. Someone who will take you to a new country with papers. Ships are searched from top to bottom."

"We stay hidden. Quiet."

"No."

"I can get married, but Vito. How will I bring him?"

"All you need is his birth certificate."

Vito insisted on knowing what they were saying. "I'm not going anywhere," he said when she explained.

"You've been beaten by grown men," she said. "How could you not want to escape?"

"I'll be big as them soon enough."

"You think it will be easier when you're grown? You think there will be more for you? Every Pinoy who looks at you will still see a souvenir baby."

"I'm quick on my feet. I make good plans. The others do what I say. They know my plans are good." Slight as he was, Vito walked like he owned the street, shoulders back, head up, stomach taut. Other kids trailed him in a pack, and when they displeased him, he could be wrathful. Still, she imagined he was young enough that, in a new place, he might become a child again, that his rage was not like hers.

"You'll get by," she said. "I want more for you. I want you never to feel fists on your face again, and that's just the start."

Vito puffed air out in an aggrieved sigh.

"What would happen when you arrived?" the American asked Tala. "Where would you go? How would you live?"

"I don't know. We will find ways."

"Was his father a soldier?"

"I don't know."

"He doesn't send money?"

"I don't know who his father is. His father doesn't know he has this son." The fathers often didn't, so this was likely the truth.

* * *

Usually, the promises of sailors were not worth as much as their dollars, but the American met Tala at the corner at dusk the next day, a package in his arms. A gift, he called it as he showed her the bananas and bread, the tins of meat and sardines, the flashlight, two canteens, a blanket. She told him they had to search for Vito. "He's not meeting us?" the man asked.

She shook her head, and started to walk. She didn't want to explain all the ways she was not in charge of Vito.

The mud of Magsaysay Drive sucked at their shoes when they crossed. A band of white skin circled the American's wrist and he kept lifting his arm, forgetting. She wondered if he was the kind of man who'd stripped off his watch before landing, or the kind who'd had it stolen. To not know even this much about him made her stomach swim. Children shouted by the Po River, the border dividing Olongapo City from the naval base. Two Americans in dress whites tossed coins off the bridge into the fetid water. They laughed at a boy who dove after the money. Where his thin body broke the surface, plumes of flies buzzed into the air. Her belly tightened, cramped, as if the boy's future had seeped into her. Droves of children milled about, watching or playing games, begging or stealing, but none were Vito. Nearness to the base conferred safety from the mayor's men, but Vito went where he wanted.

She steered the American onto side streets, where they found Vito drawing in the mud with a stick. His proud and sullen bearing, his swollen eye, the scabs that sheathed the knobs of his knees – she loved all of him. He was broken but strong, the way a bone heals thicker at the site of a break.

"Wish-heart," she said. "Come to America with me."

"You don't know what it will be like there."

"It can't be worse. Look at your face. I'm not wrong. Things will go differently for you in America."

"What about you?"

"Staying won't get me anywhere."

Vito pushed his stick deep into the dirt, dragging it through, making a trench as if he planned to hide himself by slipping down into the earth. It seemed he would not come. "Have you heard about an American grocery store? There are shelves in every direction filled top to bottom with food. We will eat meat every day. Candy." She would have said anything. Imagining such abundance, and the people accustomed to it, she felt a vague dread, but he would feel differently.

She promised herself, if Vito came, she wouldn't miss the green hills of the rainy season, the heavy heat, not even her disappeared child, whose nearness she sometimes imagined she felt, the way she could taste the salt carried on a breeze.

"You're going? No matter what?" he asked.

She nodded. It wasn't true, though.

"I guess I have to come," Vito said. "Help you conquer this new place."

She held in her smile so he wouldn't see her happiness and relief.

By the time they reached the wharves, shadows had smudged the outlines of the ships and gathered thickly under the bloom-festooned branches of the narra trees. The American placed a hand on her shoulder and guided her to a small rowboat. He lifted her into it, and he set the boy on her lap. Vito didn't stay there, but she felt his startling lightness before he scooted away. A boy made of vapors. She couldn't understand how the force of his will could be squeezed into such a wisp of a body.

When the American stepped in, water, black in the darkness, sloshed against the sides of the boat. She squeezed Vito's shoulder. He shrugged off her hand. The man began to row.

* * *

Back inside the black nights of an ocean crossing, with the sea under his feet again, Larsen missed all that enticing neon, the blazing of the lights of Olongapo City, how the sound of so many women laughing and talking had burned a wild kind of happiness into him. Tala's touch had lifted him out of the dark churn of his thoughts, and so he'd brought her on board the ship. Now though, he felt dogged by guilt and unease.

Ever since her stillbirth, his wife had left him to drift in the currents of silence that swirled between them. Larsen didn't dare reach for her, not even to help her out of the bed where she continued to convalesce, not to comfort her, certainly not to try for another child, all of which was no excuse. There was no excuse. Only a reason, only the fact of Josie turning her back, flinching at the slightest touch of his skin against her skin. She was hostile even to the soft flannel of her favorite nightgown brushing against her breasts.

Before he'd shipped out, Larsen had donated blood just to feel a nurse take his pulse, wrap a blood pressure cuff around his bicep, swab his skin with alcohol. She'd held his arm steady with her whole freckled hand as she slid the needle in.

He'd never been one to get stuck in a bad feeling before. He'd never been prone to loneliness. Solitude was welcome from time to time, but married loneliness, which could steal over you as you shared a room with the person who'd spoken solemn vows to you, that was something altogether different. He'd fled it, signed a new contract, even though work as a merchant mariner was treacherous now. The *Flying Gull* had taken sniper fire while winding up the Saigon River. Lost two hands. A swimmer had placed a mine on the deck of the *SS Baton Rouge*, and the detonation ripped a hole in her and killed every man in the engine room. Merchant ships were targets like the Navy's vessels, but they had no defenses. They bobbed along, old wrecks, hardly sea-worthy.

Larsen needed a clear head. He was chief mate, in charge of the men. Instead, he dreamed of the concentrated intoxication of Tala's small, brown hands, the salty smell of her, the way she looked at him, how her gaze tightened a band of feeling across his chest.

* * *

In the *Kestrel's* hold, heat stifled Tala. She felt as though she were trapped underground in monsoon season, with a mouth full of mud. There was a strong odor of mildew, and of something that wasn't kerosene but had the same sharp bite.

Vehicles, bound together with thick ropes, had been crammed into the space: jeeps, busted tanks, a helicopter. American forces didn't want a single broken-backed tank to fall into enemy hands, her American had told her.

Vito and Tala took refuge inside a jeep. They lay down across the seats. The leather suctioned to their skin. The powerful noises of the ship muted all the small sounds of their bodies. Usually in the dark, with no one looking, Tala relaxed; she could be only herself. Inside the ship though, the darkness had a density that made her heart race, sometimes spurring her to blink on the flashlight the American had given her, just to see with her own eyes Vito still sprawled across the backseat.

She cupped the glow in a palm, fingers turned to embers. Vito blinked, smiled. He pulled a star apple out of his pocket, squeezed the fruit until the skin split. He pried the halves apart and held one out to her, and she bit into the center of the star. The purple flesh filled her mouth: sticky, milky, sweet.

They ate bananas, and sardines. They ate tinned meat, which was oily and salty and so soft it melted against their teeth. Tala wanted always to be tasting something. In the darkness of the hold, each flavor gave off its own small flare.

Sometimes, she couldn't eat. Sometimes, the jostle of the rolling water made her too seasick. This nausea carried her back to pregnancy, when her belly had been so huge it hid her swollen feet from her view. Her baby had kicked and her feet had ached, but she hadn't minded. Others in the village had shunned her, because she wasn't married, and she'd hardly felt their slights, all self-consciousness sloughed away.

She had marveled at her body, containing within it another body. She was making a new heart, a new brain. She was making tiny toenails. She had the power to make a new person. It shocked her that all this time, the obvious had been kept hidden: a woman, any woman, had a power beside which the powers of men seemed small.

Her newborn son had pressed against her as if to push through her skin and muscle, back inside. He'd wailed as Tala's mother lifted him and whisked him to the kitchen. Tala had lain in bed, dizzy with the pain of having been ripped open, calling out for her baby. She could hear him crying, and panic clawed her insides. She tried to stand, but her legs folded.

Time passed, and she no longer heard her child. Swift as a kick, understanding hit her. He was not in the kitchen any more. He was not in the house.

When her mother returned, arms empty, Tala saw her as a stranger: this woman was a mother, Tala's own mother. Her body, Tala's first home. This woman was Tala's enemy. How could both be true?

* * *

Spray slashed Larsen's face as he emerged from the bridge to the deck. It was the fifth day of the return voyage, and they were rolling easily twenty degrees from the vertical, sky above stacked with cloud. Soon, cold rain pocked the water. A shrill hum filled the top decks from the rush of siphoned wind, and the propellers on the lifeboats spun and spun. The ship rolled heavily, hull slapping down in the troughs.

A sound snapped Larsen alert, a booming, as if bombs were exploding. The *Kestrel* began to shudder each time she rolled. This noise confounded him, then he knew. They were fucked. It sounded like the load had come loose. Those broken-down armaments they'd stashed below were slamming into the walls of the ship as they wallowed. Unchecked, they would punch through to the sea.

No one else knew a woman and child were hiding in the turbulent dark. Maybe already crushed. He'd overseen the loading. If his stowaways were killed, if the boat went down, if they all perished, it was on him.

A cargo light swung from the manhole as he climbed through into the main hold, scattering shadows over the shifting freight. The sound, walled in, was stupefying. From the ladder, he climbed onto the tank nearest the entrance, holding on with one hand, flashlight in the other.

When the neighboring tank slammed against the one he clung to, he scrambled from first to second. He moved in this way, from one vehicle to the next, through the hold, scanning for people. The jeeps had been crushed. The helicopter's flank had been caved in. A person snagged between vehicles would be mashed to jelly.

He slid to the floor, timing his motions to the roll of the boat so he could dodge the moving tanks.

He almost jumped out of his skin when he felt a hand on his shoulder.

Tala was holding the child, cocooning him with her body. She sank to her knees from the weight. Larsen could see the path back to the manhole materialize as if he'd arranged for it, and he hauled her to her feet. She didn't have her sea legs. He wove through tanks and trucks, half dragging her. At the ladder, he pried her child from her though she raked at his face and chest with her nails. The boy was limp, damp, glassy-eyed. Larsen passed him to one of the deck hands, and then wrestled with Tala until she calmed down enough to be helped up the ladder.

If she said one word about how she came to be aboard, Larsen would never work a ship again.

"Take care of them," he said, bellowing to be heard. "Get them to the second mate." Larsen and the second mate were the only officers aboard trained in first aid. The deck crew stood in a line, awaiting Larsen's lead, chains, turnbuckles, and shackles at the ready. Usually, they lashed loads to the floor, but there was no way he could see to stop the sliding without lifting all that heavy cargo into the air. He decided to chain the armaments to the loops of the steel padeyes that studded the ceiling, stringing up jeeps and tanks and the bashed-in helicopter like he was hanging hammocks. "Feed me chain," he told his men. He kept the others off the floor as much as he could. It took until sunrise to secure everything, and by then the rolling of the ship had lessened.

He emerged into the cool air of morning, and gulped water from a cup the bosun brought. The time at the hospital came alive in his mind. He couldn't fend off the memory. He'd felt his son kicking in Josie's belly, but in his arms, when he finally held him, the child was still as a stone. The nurses carried off their child without a by-your-leave, abandoning Larsen and Josie to their grief, no body to bury. He still couldn't believe it, though this was ordinary. Routine procedure, they'd told him.

* * *

Tala's jaw ached from clenching her teeth. Vito was quiet, his head in her lap, eyes unfocused, energy turned inward, as if he had to concentrate to push his blood around his veins. She'd noted his scrapes and bruises, but there was something else, an invisible wrong. His skin was clammy and hot. His breathing was rough, as though his exhalations were a gauzy fabric tearing on hooks in his throat.

They'd been locked into a small, sweltering cabin. Someone brought her a spoon and a bowl of water and mimed she must make

Vito ingest the water, spoonful by spoonful, and she tried. Liquid dribbled from the corners of his mouth.

"Your son is gravely injured," the American told her when he came. The word "son" made her think of that other boy, the son she'd birthed, who might now be one of the children running in packs through Olongapo, or might call some other woman mother, or might even be at the bottom of the Po River, adding his own stink to the water's as his muscles unknit from his bones.

"Something broke inside of him," the American said. "That's our guess, anyway. We think a rib broke and pierced his lung."

"Lung?"

He took exaggerated breaths, patted his chest.

"Help him," she said. The words were gritty in her mouth, something to spit out. She pushed a hand into Vito's hair, which was soaked with sweat. "Where's the doctor? The doctor must help."

"There's no doctor. The second mate did all he could. I don't know a thing he doesn't."

"You brought us onto this ship," she said. "Help us."

"There's nothing I can do. We're in the middle of the Pacific. Twelve days at least from San Francisco. Factor in the storm, it could be thirteen or fourteen."

"Turn us around. Turn the ship back to Subic Bay."

"We can't. That's not going to happen. It's not up to me."

She wondered what she failed to understand about him, feeling him out in a language that wasn't her first. She didn't know the kind of man he was, and he didn't know her, either. The woman she appeared to be when she entertained men in Olongapo City was just a daydream the men were having, that's how she thought about it, a dream she helped to conjure, biting back her sourness so it didn't show. "You are an officer. Chief mate."

"I don't have the power to reroute the ship. Only the captain can order that, and he won't, not for stowaways."

"There must be a way to change his mind." She was afraid. She'd followed this stranger into the middle of a vast ocean she couldn't even keep afloat in, compelling Vito to join her, and now it had gone wrong, and this man would be no help.

* * *

Wounded, Vito was more Tala's than he'd ever been. He allowed her to hold him. The limbs that pushed away from any touch no longer resisted. Weakly, he squeezed her fingers. To feel this joy of putting her hands upon him when he felt only pain shamed Tala.

Sometimes his face would close down, his breath quicken, a begging moan slip from his lips, hardly a human sound. The pain seemed to wash him out of himself. His gaze roamed aimlessly, casting furious shadows wherever it landed.

She was not sure why she and Vito were released from their cell. Pity, perhaps. When the sun shone, some of the men would carry Vito up to the deck on a stretcher. Cooped up or out in the fresh air, he slept. She hardly ever did. The smallest shifting of his body, a hitch in his breathing, the slightest sound emerging from his throat, would wake her and bring her into a needle-tight focus, as if keeping him alive depended on her constant, diligent will. Time warped, stretching and doubling, so that she crawled through its long miles painfully slowly, the minutiae of his body overwhelming her. Other times, the minutes seemed to vanish before they'd arrived, time swallowed as if dropped overboard. Watching the water, the swirl and ripple, the endlessness, a person could start to see things that weren't there. Ghosts. Visions. Spirits from old tales.

The distance was so empty, so exactly the same in every direction.

Vito was light enough. She could lift him over the rails. The water would hide them if they leapt, would knit back together, the ocean undisturbed by their entrance. There might be mercy in that leap. She didn't want to be gone like that though, didn't want Vito to be gone while all these other people still breathed and moved and lived. Still, he suffered, and she wondered.

The sailors watched her out of the corners of their eyes. She felt their fear, and their hunger. They kept their distance, except for her American, who would check on her and Vito when his shifts ended. In that tiny cabin, with Vito soundly asleep, she had sex with the American, just once more. She took a pleasure from it that had nothing to do with bodies or the sensations they hold. She felt as though she was stealing something from him, and she wanted to grip it and yank, pull out whatever dark thing would unspool, fill the space left behind with a rage that could flame as bright as her own. He cried his silent tears afterwards. She wanted to crush all tenderness, and now when he wept she rose, dressed, turned away.

She left Vito asleep in the American's care, not often, but sometimes, desperate to be a sole person not wrapped around another person, just for a few minutes. Closeness with Vito, the pleasure of his head in her lap, his hand in her hand, couldn't curb this restlessness when it came. She'd say she needed a shower, a bathroom, some privacy, anything, and she'd haunt the ship, padding barefoot through walkways smelling of vomit and brine, of onions burnt in the galley.

Freed, she touched things, turned dials, broke switches, loosened bolts until they dropped into her hands, moved objects from their places, stoked her fury with these small acts of violence against this ship that held her and Vito hostage in the nowhere of the sea. She felt unlike herself. The ghost of her lost baby was inside her, making mischief – she sometimes felt sure of it. She waited for some kind of answer of what to do to float up from whatever had come to occupy the hollow inside her. At first, all that came were these urges. She loosened knots in ropes, tugging until her fingers burned. She sifted through dented forks and spoons dripping dry in the galley while the messman peeled potatoes. When his back turned, she palmed the paring knife she found. Beyond the galley, in the laundry, she tipped powdered detergent into a running washing machine, soap flakes pouring into the gray water and cloth, forming a powdery island that crumbled, then frothed up, a frenzy of foam that grew and grew and spilled over.

She figured out which was the captain's cabin. Sometimes he was in the control room, where she would never be allowed. But for long stretches, longer than seemed right, he shut himself inside his private cabin, and no one disturbed him, not even the officers.

The men eyed her, true, but they also ducked out of her way when she neared, quickening their steps, pulling their elbows close when she passed in the tight corridors that burrowed through the ship. To the sailors on board, she was a bad omen. The American had told her. She'd thought it was because of Vito's injury, but Larsen said it was only because she was a woman. To deny that they were at the ocean's mercy and the ocean had no mercy, they clung to superstitions. As if, given they remembered never to whistle, never to cut their hair or nails at sea, never to speak the word "drown" out loud, they could keep themselves safe until they'd docked.

The afternoon Tala entered the captain's cabin, she was thinking of seductions. Her breath came in fast bursts, her daring a flame inside her, bright and hot and tipped with worry about Vito, whom she'd left alone. The captain was snoring, sprawled on his back in bed, the flesh of his face and neck worn from sun, slackened by time, all of him sagging downwards except his jutting nose, which seemed to part space in defiance of gravity. The room stank of sweat and drinking. Whisky bottles clustered in a crate on the floor, many empty. He didn't stir when she touched his arm. She'd seen many different men sleep. Whatever they'd been like awake, asleep they were all inert, helpless.

It wasn't hard to find rope on a ship. When she returned, the captain slept still, sprawled in the same position.

The puzzle before her: how to ensnare him without waking him.

She slid her hands beneath his closest leg, and dragged it toward its mate. She wound the rope around his ankles three times and knotted it with fisherman's knots she'd learned from her father. Though one knot might suffice, she made four because such thick rope was difficult to tighten. She bound his legs to the bedpost. As she tied his wrists together, her hostage stirred, shifting from back to hip, and she waited to see if he would wake.

* * *

Larsen watched Tala cross the deck and thought of the bad luck everyone whispered about. By the looks of her, the boy had died. He walked to meet her, and her gaze tore into him. He pictured Vito as he'd been when well – eyes agleam with scornful delight, rakish, restless, a child but not quite seeming so – and the idea that this boy had ceased to live seemed impossible, injury or no. But why else would she leave him below, alone?

Pity swallowed his words, but then she smiled, and reached for his hand. She led him through the ship to the captain's quarters. She pushed open the hatch as if the room beyond were her very own bedroom.

The captain was passed out, and more startling, tied up. She didn't know a Flemish knot or an anchor's bend, but her knots were sturdy.

"What have you done?"

"Turn the ship back," she said.

"I can't do that."

"We must. The captain no longer decides where we go."

"There's no 'we.'"

"No one would believe that. They have ears," she said. "They have eyes. Don't you think they guess I am here because of you?"

"Turning the ship requires a willing crew. Not one man and a girl who knows nothing."

"My father had a boat."

"This is a Victory ship with 8,000 horsepower steam turbines. Not a dinghy."

"They are afraid of me. The men. You use that. There must be a few you can make help. Tell them about the captain. Tell them he is a prisoner."

A comfort, he'd thought her. Someone he could save. She stood looking at him, her cheeks smooth planes, eyes all afire. He'd been stupid and blind. He'd mistaken smallness and prettiness for weakness and sweetness.

He already regretted everything that would happen next, even now, when it was still not decided. He felt a throbbing, like hands were pressing down on him in a rhythm, pushing air out of his lungs, pushing on his heart as if to make it beat faster. Even if Larsen could sway a couple men, there was a whole crew to contend with.

He dragged a breath into his chest. He could talk a hand or two into staying, couldn't he? Then, clear the ship with a ruse, by triggering the alarm. He could almost hear the whistle sound across the *Kestrel*, and the footfalls of his men as they rushed to tear tarps off the lifeboats and haul them into the water. Abandon ship, that's what they would hear when the whistle sounded. Every sailor would remember how the load had crashed around during the pitch of the storm. They'd be certain the ship had been damaged and they were sinking after all.

He could smell Tala's sweat. She brushed her tangled hair from her face, touched his arm. To send his men to the lifeboats unnecessarily was a betrayal so large, he couldn't hold the thought fast in his mind. In his reach, mounted on the wall, was one of the switches that would sound the alarm. He seemed to see it even when he wasn't looking that way, as if it glowed with a terrible light.

Tala watched her American. Her chances, and Vito's, would be best if he helped. She would do what she needed to do. He would care more about consequences. She let herself feel a pang of sympathy for him, and she let it dissolve, let her fingers shift to touch the knife she'd wrapped in a rag and wedged into the back pocket of her pants, where the tip of it pricked her as she stepped toward the captain in his bed.

She heard the staccato of her mother's voice ringing out in her memory. She hadn't seen her mother in years, but Tala didn't doubt the woman still had a smolder to her gaze. That perfectly round mole on her mother's cheek – surely she still wore it like a jewel. "I chose the best I could for him and for you," she'd said to Tala. "An unmarried girl with a baby, what life would that child have? Or you? I freed you from the persecution of whispers."

Tala had not known what to say, how to best rip the thin skin of truth off this lie. In the weeks that followed, all her efforts to find her child had come to nothing. She'd hardly rested, and so she didn't heal, and even when she finally left the village for Olongapo City, each step she took, blood soaked the wad of cloth she had stuffed into her underwear.

Now, the knife was warm from Tala's fingers. She could see the captain's chest rising, falling, rising, falling. Under her feet, in the humming deep of the ship, Vito breathed. The simplest act, done by everyone, everywhere, without a thought. It always became impossible eventually, but not for Vito, not yet.

The hostage opened his eyes. The ship rolled lightly on the water, shifting and quaking as if it were awakening, and that prickly thing that had come to occupy Tala's insides pushed for the surface, that ghost child, that wanting, that fearsome will, like it was coming up for air, like it would pour darkly from her mouth, and she thought, maybe I am a pox upon this ship, maybe I am a witch, a curse, bad luck to all sailors, maybe I am fury.

Alicia Oltuski

SIM

The people who lived in the apartment below ours, she was an academic and he was migraine-prone, and those were two of the reasons they didn't like my mother, who favored classic rock music
in the evenings. The other was that she'd called the police on them
once when he threw his wife at her nightstand, or the nightstand at
his wife. Their daughter was my friend. I was only allowed at their
apartment when my mother was desperate for what she called alone
time, but wasn't; otherwise, the girl came to me. They'd named her
Alexandra but seemed to have forgotten, and called her Sim instead.
When we were at Sim's, we had a series of games we played, all
of which utilized the half dozen decorative rugs in their home that
were the harvest of Sim's father's carpet store on Spring Street. (This
was another reason they didn't like my mother; it was Sim's father's
carpeting, in particular, that she'd rejected. He'd tried to sell her a
pair of matching rugs when we moved in, first by insisting we were
too loud, then by insisting they were too beautiful.) In one of our

---

Alicia Oltuski is the author of a collection of stories, *Precious Objects* (Simon & Schuster,
2011). Her stories have appeared in *Tin House*, *TheNewYorker.com*, *W Magazine*, *Glimmer Train*, *McSweeney's Internet Tendency*, *NPR Berlin Stories*, *Narrative Magazine*, and
Catapult.

games, you could win by rolling yourself up in the distressed arabesque rug that covered Sim's bedroom floor. In another, you won if you were the first to pull a green thread from the cluster of multicolor tassels that hung off the living room carpet – the largest in their home, and the one which Sim's mother always seemed to sidestep if she could. Because of our pulling at it, the color balance of the rug's tassels had shifted and sometimes, we hypothesized that Sim's father noticed and was planning his revenge, but we kept plucking the green threads, because that was the way the game went. Most of our games could only be played at Sim's home, due to the rugs. The only game we/Sim could think of that did not involve her father's inventory was getting naked and riding our building's elevator three flights down and back up before anyone saw you. Sim kept a tally of who was winning the games in a notebook. Whoever won at the end would get a prize, but only she knew the prize, and only she knew what constituted the end.

The end was not when our building's superintendent caught Sim naked in the elevator one day. As she relayed it, he just said to her, "It's not a whorehouse, this," but also brushed past her breast on his way out. Meanwhile, I rode the second elevator, alone and cold, but more alone than cold. It remained a fantasy of mine years later for Mr. Abbott to see me naked, but when I came back to Maryland to move my mother out of that same building after I finished a later-life PhD, he came to say goodbye, and it occurred to me that, actually, I hated him, I rather wanted to kill him; imagine if it had been me.

In September Sim's father's store came home with him altogether, when his business went under. He laid them out, the majority of the carpets in his study. They covered the entirety of the floor, and were piled so high, you had to climb into the room. Often, after a phone call, he would kneel outside the threshold of the door, sorting through his stock by rolling down a corner of each rug, as though sifting through the pages of a book. Then he would call to Sim and her mother (and consequently to me) to drag out the chosen inventory, while he kept the rugs above it anchored inside the room by squatting down on them, his fists and feet pinned to the mound. The latter expended visible effort, Sim's father driving his own weight through the carpets and into the floor. When we got out the rug, we would roll it and he would tie it up, like hunted meat, and add it onto his dolly to take out to his car. Sometimes, after a day or two – one time, a week – the carpet might come back, and he would return it to the top of the pile on his own and then, when he had gone to bed or left the apartment, Sim's mother would perform a lesser version of his original toil to cover the returned item with whatever rug lay beneath it, presumably so her husband could more easily forget it. I understood the equation: if the carpet selling went well, he was less dangerous.

My mother had started requiring more alone time that summer, she had started seeing a man named Keith, so I was there with greater and greater frequency over the next few months, learning the details of their routine. It had been a long while since she'd called the police on them.

By November, we'd depleted the living room rug's green tassels, and it changed the entire impression Sim's apartment left on me when I visited. The place looked oranger, and I felt compelled to stay long every time I went, even when my mother's apartment was empty, or she was alone. She had also stopped asking me, every time I returned, whether anything had happened, partially because nothing had happened in so long and partially, I think, because she didn't want an answer that would necessitate change. (And nothing had ever happened to me, even when something happened at Sim's house.) But if I said that he'd taken a knife and carved BITCH into the parquet inside the master bedroom (which he had, Sim showed me, and which I didn't say), or that sometimes, upon my entering, I'd find a shattered object somewhere in the room that had so recently been shattered, it hadn't yet been taken to the trash, then she would have had to forbid me from going there. It wasn't Keith, really. I don't think it was sex – there was sex, but it wasn't sex that made her not want me there. It wasn't me either. By far, the simplest way to put it would be that our quarters were very close – mine and my mother's, Sim and her family's – and that some of us needed to roam, or else we would rage.

We had somehow outgrown the need to tempt fate with the elevator, but not the need to play with the carpets when her father was gone. Maybe they were all one game, and the game was to see what men would do to us. We wrote curse words onto the bottom side of the entry runner, shaved splinters off the side of the steps to the trash room and dispersed them in the psychedelic-patterned rug that bore the weight of her parents' bed, on her father's side.

He was working at a restaurant down Cedar, running orders to law offices that had recently discovered our nominal section of the commuter rail line and had sprouted outposts. He was still trying to sell the rugs, at night, in a wholesale dump. We heard him on the phone, describing their qualities, then their quantities, and, finally, their price. Sometimes, people would come over to their apartment to look, and Sim's father would stand outside the study while they sifted. I liked to be there when they came to look at the rugs. It felt like showing off – even though what I was showing off was not mine – in the way I had felt every time I saw Mr. Abbott after his elevator ride with Sim. I didn't realize that when the rugs were gone, she would be, too.

It took almost a month for someone to make an offer. Sim's father was out at work when she came. Sim's mother was in the bedroom, in the far corner of the bed where I sometimes spied her if Sim ever opened the door to say we were leaving, and where she looked like a pile of laundry with hair and teeth. We left now, we went out. We had bored of our building; we realized it stank. Sometimes, when I got home from school, she was already waiting outside for me in front of our building (hers was closer), and we'd walk to the park and sit on a bench and Sim would tell me who was smoking what. That day, though, we were home, because Sim's mother had complained that we always left – and she wasn't wrong, and she also wasn't wrong to want us there when he came home from work, and Sim knew this – it was she who told me – but the building stank and now that we were older, we hated to tolerate anything we didn't have to.

The buyer, when we opened the door for her, asked for Sim's father, but Sim just said, "I'll show you where the rugs are." By this time, they'd all been rolled up and leaned against the wall of the study, which, I would learn later in life – the first time I'd enter a real rug store – was how everyone else did it. The rugs were propped two scrolls deep, and looked like they were closing in on her in the small room. She bent each one back and took a picture with a camera she'd brought out of her bag.

"Are there any others?" she asked, wandering into the living room.

Sim pointed at the ground beneath us. We were standing on the erstwhile green-tasseled rug. The woman aimed her camera down.

"And then there's this," said Sim, pointing to the one beneath her father's armchair, but there was a shattered lamp in the corner be-hind the chair and some of the glass had gotten stuck in the carpet, and the buyer did not photograph that rug.

I could see Sim thinking of other rugs to show the buyer, and I could see the buyer looking around the apartment, not at the rugs: at the shattered lamp, at the toaster oven plugged into the outlet be-side the TV; at the pile of their winter coats on the floor, next to the couch. "Is everything okay?" she asked.

"Mm-hm," said Sim.

The buyer was straining to see into the bedroom through the gap we left when we forgot to close the door all the way. "Is that your mother?" she asked Sim.

"She's resting."

"Are you sure?" said the buyer.

I watched to see what Sim would say. I wondered if the buyer thought Sim was my older sister, or if she knew I didn't live there.

"How long until your father gets back?" said the buyer.

"I don't know."

The woman handed Sim the camera. "Go take a picture of her face. I can send the film to you," she said, looking at me. Then I knew she knew we weren't sisters.

"What about the carpets?" asked Sim.

But the woman ignored the question. She had me write down my address on her inventory list. I remember wondering, despite my nerves, what she thought of my handwriting. Sim took the camera and came back with it a moment later. When the buyer left, Sim said I should go, too.

My mother was breaking up with Keith over the phone because he hadn't known the Berlin Wall had come down. I didn't tell her that I hadn't known, either. On Saturday morning, she offered to make me breakfast, but I didn't want her breakfast. I tried to see if Sim wanted to go out. She was babysitting her mother until her father left to go to a game. My mother was trying to figure out more about the Berlin Wall. She'd called a friend who was married to a Russian in the hopes of disambiguating and was on the phone taking notes when Sim came upstairs to get me. I held the door for Sim, but she said she'd wait in the hallway. Pulling aside her jacket, she flashed a knife.

I followed her downstairs and into the public garage two blocks north of our building, where I had never been; my mother hadn't owned a car since before I was born. I thought that maybe we would rob someone – that she would rob someone and that I would stand there and watch.

"My dad loaded the truck this morning," Sim said, as we approached a truck. I had never seen the truck, but neither had it occurred to me, as it should have, that there must have been one.

"She didn't ever send the pictures?" Sim asked me. I think often about whether it was a postal error or my handwriting that prevented the photos from arriving (they never did), or if the woman just forgot about Sim.

"She could, still," I said. I think I said that because of the presence of the knife.

It had been two weeks, and another buyer came by, a warehouse rep from Anne Arundel. Sim's dad was home and Sim's mom stayed in her room and the package that was negotiated – gutlessly, according to Sim – included the transport of the rugs by their owner on Sunday morning.

Sim lifted herself onto the back of the truck and then took out her knife. I suddenly wished I'd brought a knife, even though I didn't know what she was going to do with it, and even though I knew that whatever she did, I couldn't do.

He was driving them the next day. We were going to ruin everything for him, she said. By everything, she meant the rugs. We couldn't cut the outer bands, Sim said, otherwise, he'd notice in the garage, before he left. It had to be the mass of the inner rugs pushing on the out-facing layer as he sped up on Cedar Street.

I watched her stick her arm deep into the network of rugs – they looked like pipes – with the knife in her hand, and cut. I saw it every time she broke one of the plasticuffs, because her arm popped.

"Tell me when they feel like they're getting pushed," she said. I climbed into the cargo bed. "Stand on my other side, I only smell from my right pit."

I only partially understood the plan until I felt what she was talking about: the push of the inner stacks on the carpets that surrounded them. It scared me to feel how much mass there was amongst them collectively. When she was finished, we sat down inside the cab. She went into the glove compartment and looked around for, clearly, the first time; this car was more for the carpets than it was for them. Inside, he kept a Coke bottle filled with water, a single breath mint, ten dollars, and a roll of toilet paper. Sim added the knife, and then we left.

By the time I got back home, my mother had stopped her inquiries into Communism. "Clem," she said. Some pastry was uncoiling in the microwave. She was drinking juice out of a plastic cup because she hated washing glasses. She said it felt like hospital work. I got the pastry and we split it and she said that Keith had brought her down in the exact way she thought he was going to lift her up. She also said, six months after she'd first called the police, "You know, I think Sim's father is abusive."

I waited a block away from the garage. They were late, and I was already cold. I thought of Sim in the car with her parents, sitting between them. I had never been in close proximity to either one of them, had no idea what they smelled like, the force their bodies exerted upon the space around them when they tensed. When I saw the garage door lift for a bundle of rugs, like a cartoon, I wished I'd told my mother that I wasn't going to school on the chance that he came after me.

They didn't make it to Cedar. The carpets slumped left when they hit the driveway's apron, as though systemically ill, and then came apart by the time they finished their right turn, tumbling at the intersection by our building. He slammed the brakes. The car behind them rode over the pile of rugs – how easily, as though they were a speed bump – and into their car. Someone honked after it happened, but I wasn't sure which vehicle.

I was more scared than cold, but I was very cold. I tried and failed to see inside Sim's father's car from where I stood. There was an immense yellow rug hanging over the side of the cab. After a moment, Sim's father opened the door and batted the yellow rug out of his face, as though cutting brush. He directed Sim's mother to stop traffic – which hadn't, for the most part – while he spoke to the other driver, who had also emerged from his car with his insurance card. Most of the other cars were skirting around the rugs in the intersection, though some drove over the mass. Sim's mother took Sim's hand, as though she were a child – she was and she wasn't – and led her back in the car, and closed her in. Then she stepped over the pile of butchered rugs, and into the street. Her hand wasn't held up as his had been. She continued across Cedar, past Cedar, onto the ramp, and at the other end, where they could no longer see the stoppage we'd created, she turned and went at the cars, and they at her.

Sim opened the door of the truck and screamed. The guy with the insurance card put his insurance card in his mouth and ran toward the ramp. Sim's father then followed. All the cars had stopped now.

I ran to the truck. "Is she underneath the car or in front of it?" Sim asked. I got into the truck next to her. "What are you doing? Go look!" she screamed. I couldn't look any more than she could, but I did get out of the car, so that I wasn't flaunting doing nothing. The police had come, I realized, when the sirens I hadn't heard stopped. I turned around. No one on the ramp or on Cedar was moving. Only one full block down, where the incline leveled and Sim's mother's body was no longer in view, had they begun to get restless and make themselves known.

One day – this was a few months after Sim and her father had moved to southern Maryland, near a flailing historic district – Mr. Abbott was in our apartment, and he told us about everything that Sim and her family had broken during their occupancy in the building. My mother listened from our couch, enraptured.

"Isn't that wild?" she asked when Mr. Abbott left.

"What?"

"The curtain shredded in the disposal?"

I shrugged.

"Did you see that when you were over there playing?"

"I don't know."

"Why can't you just tell me?" She was getting frustrated.

"Because I don't know," I said.

But it wasn't a curtain. It was Sim's mother's nightgown, and I didn't want my mother to tell Mr. Abbott; I didn't even want my mother to tell herself, all over again, lying in her bed, thinking, boy, had we had ourselves a year.

Jacqueline Keren

ASH WEDNESDAY

They ate everything. Bonnie was never hungry. Coffee killed her appetite. When she smoked, her brain idled before she was off again to the next chore.

She stood in front of the refrigerator and the pictures on the door stared back at her, Kaleb, a lopsided face, like his father, the right eye smaller than the left, Kayla, like her, a round, sunflower face. Hands in the air, their mouths cavernous.

A jar of pickles in the fridge.

The baby slept. His breezy breath, warm and wet as she held him to her chest. Kayla weighed more than Bonnie did, huffing when she ran, yet she was a little thing, barely reaching Bonnie's shoulders. They followed her around the kitchen when she lugged in the groceries – babbling about school, the beach, grandparents – and ate everything the day she bought it.

A box of cereal on the counter. She shook it. Dust.

She took her pill, a frozen ball of crystal. Her ex had taught her to pack the meth into pellets she stored in the freezer. One pop per day. He was applying for a patent, he said. He was an entrepreneur, not

Jacqueline Keren's work has appeared in *Santa Monica Review, Calyx Journal, Confrontation*, and *Redivider*.

the loser she said he was. The speed kicked in gradually, and she ran faster than all the things that needed to be done in the morning. The good feeling was good enough.

They sat on the couch, Kayla pulling on her socks. Bonnie's toes scrunched the thick carpet as if they were digging to China. They got busy after she took her pill. Her feet tingled with the electricity she generated.

"Mom," Kayla said. "Your toes are going crazy."

She leaned against her daughter, and when they collided, Kayla's hair rose in an airy fan. A transfer of energy, mother to daughter. Kayla would do well today. Bonnie sang, "Come and meet my dancing feet."

Kayla giggled. Kaleb stood in the doorway. If only he scowled, but his face was flat. A quiet boy. A somber boy. At night, he sat at the kitchen table flying through his homework while she and Kayla labored over her assignments. Bonnie's arm a half moon around her daughter's shoulders. When Kayla pressed her pencil to the paper, she kissed the silky side of her head.

She scuffed outside in her slippers as the bus rounded the corner and waddled down their block. The kids boarded, and as the bus bounced away, they waved from the back windows. For a quick moment, Kaleb smiled. She lifted her hand, patted the baby's back.

She pulled on a sweater. It was just the two of them and the errands. She couldn't go to the store in her slippers, not like the cows from Pill Hill who shopped in their pajamas. In her shoes, her wiggly toes would rub, blister, bleed. She wrapped them in duct tape and pulled on her sneakers.

She turned off the coffee machine, flicked the lights, twisted the knobs on the stove. The pilot light clicked, the blue flame shivering. She snuffed it out. Check, check, check.

She strapped the baby into the car seat and tossed the stroller into the trunk. Someday she'd take him somewhere: across the bridge, into the mountains, a long road with a rest stop.

She circled the grocery store parking lot before pulling in between a pickup truck and a white van. A rocket jetting across the van's side pierced a thicket of grey clouds, on course for the nebula of a swirling drain. Space Plumber. She killed the engine and rested in the warm bubble of the car. A knot of people descended the steps of the church as the organ moaned. Even from across the street, she could see the black smudges on their foreheads. They were heading toward the Miss Port Archer Diner. A woman pushing a shopping cart, a mattress balanced across it, panicked in the middle of the road and straddled the orange line as the cars rolled by until someone took pity and slowed to a stop. The sun cleared the top of the grocery store, and Bonnie closed her eyes against the piercing brightness. She clutched her shoulder bag, inside, her shopping list and the vouchers from the county. Time to brave the store, collect what she needed. She scratched her scalp, picking at a scab. She closed her eyes and tried to see ahead in time: she'd fill her basket, wait in line. Her turn to pay. The checkout line would lengthen while the clerk processed the vouchers, punching in the long, secret codes, and the cows, massing behind her, huffed and puffed. She started, her eyes snapping open. The sun had risen another notch. She wiped the drool from her chin and kneaded the strap of her shoulder bag. Always this exhaustion before the pill kicked into high gear. A warm wind stirred through the window. She shucked off her sweater. It was a gift, a day in March like May.

She popped open the stroller then got to work on the baby, undoing the buckles and straps of the car seat, only to set him in the vinyl sling and snap him up all over again. She slung her shoulder bag over the handles of the stroller. She wheeled with one hand, the other, flung by her side, propelling her across the parking lot to her destination. Shoppers wheeled their carts behind the big windows. A silent movie, and she was making her entrance. The manager stood near the door. Was he watching her? She swerved, crossing the street to peer inside the windows of the diner. Two men sat at the counter. Space Plumber hunched over a plate streaked with yellow. He was a godsend, her mother said, a plumber who answered the phone during hunting season. Next to him sat his assistant whom the wicked old ladies who occupied the booths weekday mornings called Crack Harbor. Breakfast was winding down. The lunch rush an hour away at least. A window of time when she would be tolerated. She rifled through her bag and found the envelope with the vouchers but no wallet. She closed her eyes and rewound through the morning, back to her kitchen, where she floated like a spirit under the table, over the counters and into the drawers. The dishwasher? The oven? The wallet was somewhere, but it was hidden.

She sat at the far end of the counter, near the kitchen, separated from the two men by a line of empty stools, their polished wooden surfaces reflecting the sun. In the booths, the women, black crosses on their foreheads, cackled. How much did she owe? Nothing. She was paid up. She'd ask Katrinka to start a new tab, but that girl was hard. She'd say "no" before she could go above her head to the owner.

A new girl set a mug of coffee in front of her. A tattoo ran across the "v" of her shirt: *Knock 'em dead*.

"Where's Katrinka?" she asked.

"Day off."

The baby gurgled, his toothless mouth an oval of delight. The girl cooed, the same unfocused openness in her eyes, the same search for goodness in everything she encountered.

"Hey."

The waitress glanced up at her.

"I'd like two eggs, poached. Tell him to put a little maple syrup in the water. White toast. I'll butter it myself."

The girl scribbled away then ran the ticket into the kitchen. A spatula scraping across the grill screeched to a stop. The owner leaned his grey head out the door. "Bonnie?"

A question. She'd cleared her account at the beginning of the month. She answered with a question of her own. "Tab?"

His eyes were the pale blue of the sky as the sun rose. "That's it for the week." His gaze shifted down the counter to Space Plumber. Something passed between them, a thought that sailed above her head, the sound trailing, and she ran after it until it faded away.

"For sure," she said while the girl filled her mug with a bitter stream of coffee. "And juice for the baby," she said. "And a straw."

The waitress nodded before running the coffee pot down to the booths where the women crowed.

The girl, returning with the coffee pot, leaned in as she refilled Bonnie's cup and peered sideways down the counter. "They have marks on their foreheads," she whispered.

"What?" Bonnie saw burns, bullet holes, thumb prints before she collected the pieces, the people streaming from the church, organ music on a weekday morning, the onset of Lent. "Ash Wednesday."

The girl gazed at her, her eyes big and brown and empty.

"You know what that is?"

She brightened. "A Jewish thing?"

Bonnie laughed, a throaty cough. The baby caught his breath and gurgled. A screech from the old ladies. "You're something," she said.

The girl frowned, her brows knotted. Was she going to cry?

"I'm a Baptist," the girl said.

Bonnie patted her hand. She pointed out the window at the church. "A Catholic thing," she said. Her arm slid across the street, "Presbyterian," and down the hill, "Methodist," before waving vaguely west at the old mines and the tailing piles, where the Baptists met in the minister's house. "You." She sighed. "Don't worry about it."

The girl nodded as Bonnie's plate slid out from the kitchen.

The yolks, when she punctured them, bled sunrise-orange across the plate. She staunched the flow with her toast and pinched off a bit for the baby. Everything tasted like dust. She set her fork down just to smell the butter-crisped edges and fried potatoes. When she was a kid, they had come here on the Sunday mornings when she woke to her father's big rig in the driveway. She ran outside in her pajamas and climbed into the cab, where he slept on the bench behind the front seat. Sleep came quickly, he said, when he was parked at a rest stop. One yank of the horn and he was crawling out of his sleeping bag and buttoning his flannel shirt. If he didn't show up, they ate out anyway. Her mother pulled the waitress aside as they were leaving, and they waited outside by the claw foot tub, overflowing with purple petunias, until the wheels the diner once rode on began to spin and steam billowed from the wells as it had in the days when it rolled from factory to factory, her mother explained.

When she was done, she knocked on the counter. "End of the month," she hollered into the kitchen. Her knuckles throbbed, her skin as thin as tissue paper. She was almost at the door when the girl called, "The baby!" They gaped at her, the girl and Space Plumber and the old ladies. She was only headed to the bathroom. She returned for the stroller and pushed him in with her. She sat on the toilet, tickling the baby. See? Not forgotten. A wooden wardrobe guarded him while she washed her hands and when she was done, she buried a roll of toilet paper in her shoulder bag and covered it with the baby's blanket. She would give up thieving for Lent.

She pushed the stroller across the parking lot, pausing before the grocery store to claw through her hair. When she found the scab, she picked at the edges, whittling away the island of dried blood. She scraped the red flakes from beneath her nails. The baby gurgled. She closed her eyes and combed the house again for her wallet. The bureau, the bedroom, the hallway table. This time, she found it on the kitchen counter between a box of cereal and a soda bottle. Kayla adored bubbly drinks. Some days, Bonnie could see Kayla grow with each vigorous tug on her straw.

The wallet was empty. She could see that in her mind. That left the vouchers with all their rules. The cashier sorting through her purchases. The cows snorting. What if she picked up the wrong kind of milk and the line grew while she ran for the right one? Cash was quicker. A card was easy. It was only the middle of the month, and she was nearly tapped out. Weeks before the next infusion. When it pinged on her card, they would celebrate. Sunday breakfast at the diner. Steak and eggs for everyone. During the week, the kids ate breakfast and lunch at school. Fish sticks for dinner. Banana for the baby.

She rolled the stroller around the village, the streets unfurling in a familiar pattern: house, house, church, repeat. Only the style of church varied. The melting snow had left thick drifts of sand in the gutters that she forced the wheels of the stroller through. She slowed in front of a house where a woman sat on her porch, feathered hair greying at the temples, a black blotch on her forehead. A Jewish thing. Dumb girl. Mrs. Deroche stroked the dog in her lap. Her dark eyes rested on Bonnie. A bicycle wheeled by and the dog leapt into action. Mrs. Deroche waited a few heartbeats before she called, "Nipper! Nipper!" and the dog retreated into her lap. Bonnie was the same age as her daughter who drove around town in an enormous SUV to collect the dead for the county.

She rocked the stroller back and forth, the wheels scraping.

"Yes, Bonnie?"

She dragged her foot through the sand. "Can I use your bathroom?" she asked.

Mrs. Deroche's smile evaporated, leaving behind a tight line. A heartbeat or two before she nodded. She would allow her in to use the toilet and no more, once and never again. If Bonnie were in her shoes, would she have made the same choice? Never.

She followed the train of the old woman's bathrobe, the darkened hem gliding over the floor, on a path cut through stacks of magazines and children's games. She left her the baby to coo at.

She ran the tap while she rummaged through the medicine cabinet. Baby aspirin, Q-tips, tweezers, blush. Her underarms were hot and damp, and she swiped them with a stick of deodorant. On the bottom row, the orange bottles with their smart white labels. Pills for problems, pills for pain. She gleaned her record: her heart beat too fast, she ate too many sweets. Bonnie suffered, too. Her neck ached from sleeping on a flattened pillow, her toes strained against their binding. Her mother told her to slow down, but the dishes and laundry and dusting fought for her attention. She crammed two bottles into her pockets. The old lady wasn't using them. Why else would she have so many?

She wore a gleaming smile back to the living room.

The old lady eyed her. "You left the faucet running," she said.

She felt the frown rising to the surface but tamped it down before galloping back to the bathroom. One last glance at the medicine cabinet and its hidden treasures, her sallow reflection in the mirror, her teeth not as sparkly as she imagined. Should she try her luck? What luck?

"Don't forget the baby," the woman called as she hurried to the front door.

She grabbed the stroller, wrestled it through the entryway and down the steps.

She wandered through the streets to a hill overlooking the lake. The sun beamed through the bare trees and warmed her skin. A truck drove onto the ice and parked near a fishing shack, smoke billowing from the chimney. On his rare stops at home, her father had fished. In time, she lost track of the days without him, and what did it matter? She'd preserved a memory of him in his cab, like a Ball jar of dilly beans or pickled eggs. When the baby was old enough for school, she would meander through the shacks scattered around the icy bay, pausing to rest in one before heading out on the road on the opposite shore. The baby burbled. He had the look that warned of red-faced squealing, a mood only motion could quell.

She posted on the website for the county tag sale: *for sale!* The name, copied carefully from the label of Mrs. Deroche's pill bottle. She waited and when nothing happened, pulled a chair out onto the stoop. The baby was napping. Her neighbor across the street, sitting on her porch, waved as a car went by. An old man walked his dog down the sidewalk. Then no one, except the egg yolk sun pulsing on her head. The sweat made her scalp itch. The idleness made her toes ache, but when the first people arrived, her toes rested. In less than an hour, the first bottle was empty. The cash in her hand was enough to buy spring clothes for the kids.

A man wandered by late, his pale yellow dog trailing behind him. "I'm going to the reservation," he said.

The dog sniffed her hand before squatting beside his master. She held out a ten dollar bill. "Pick me up some cigarettes?"

He ruffled the bill, held it up to the sun, then slipped it into his hip pocket.

"What's your commission?" she asked.

"Ten percent."

The usual. She picked at her scab while he idled on the sidewalk. The dog wagged its tail.

"I saw you on the computer," he said.

"On the tag sale?"

"On Google maps, right where you are now."

"I'm always here." Every morning, every afternoon.

He glanced at his dog and nodded. "You were here the day the Google car drove by."

She tapped her front teeth. She read the goings-on online, the prayers and accusations, the blessings and family feuds, but she hadn't noticed the eye that looked back at her as if she were a piece of the scenery, like a street sign rattled by the wind off the lake. "So?"

He shrugged as he strolled away, the dog loping beside him.

She was heading inside when a woman turned up her path, her face overrun by her owly sunglasses, her long, black hair tangled in a rat's nest. The wind blew her cardigan open. Her blouse was stained, coffee and ketchup. When she worked at the Dollar Store, scanning toilet paper and toothpaste, she was tidier. One day, when Bonnie was buying milk and cheese, she came upon a pair of fuzzy slippers. When she'd slipped her feet into the roomy toe box, her toes rested, but relief lasted only a moment before they were running again. This woman had found her in tears in the aisle. After she explained, the woman bought her a roll of duct tape. A miracle. She could wear shoes again without beating her forehead and scratching her head. That was before the woman's son had died. They had buried him on a colder day than this one. She had sported the sunglasses ever since. Bonnie was grateful that she did.

She gave her a deal, three pills for $15. "Will you have more?" the woman asked.

A good salesman guaranteed a steady supply. "I hope so."

Space Plumber's van was still in the parking lot when she returned to the grocery store, and she slid in beside it. Was he working nearby or slurping coffee? With the cash crumpled in her pocket, the doors parted for her. She shook a cart free of the clump and drove it toward the rainbow mounds of produce. She held a cantaloupe to her nose, the skin roughing her cheek, and inhaled the sweet, caramel scent. Music floated through the aisles: "Goodbye Yellow Brick Road." The speckled yellow squares of linoleum a path through this cornucopia. When she touched her toe to the first square, she felt the pull of all the plenty. She wrapped her hands around the metal handle of the cart, cold despite the plastic grip, and glided on. The store hummed, the muffled purr of machinery. Formula, milk, orange juice, diapers. She grabbed a loaf of bread by the waist. Soda and chips. An apple and a banana for the baby.

A crooked line stretched from the register to the beach ball display. Summer, the kids underfoot, desperate for things to do. She tossed a ball into her cart. They'd sit at the beach, squeal as they scampered in and out of the lake. The baby with a shovel, maybe even a bucket, sand clinging to his pudgy legs.

Someone joined the line behind her, set his basket at his feet and kicked it when the line crept forward. As it scraped across the floor, her head began to pound. She turned. Space Plumber, a gallon of milk in his hand, a blotch on his broad forehead, rested his eyes upon her. He had answered her mother's call one spring when the sump pump broke and the cellar flooded, and he waded through the water to install a new pump, dolls and Christmas ornaments and ancient atlases floating in the current.

"What are you giving up for Lent?" he asked.

"Smoking," she said.

"Brave."

Even with the light pouring through the windows, the store was cold. The line crept forward, a snake in the sun. Her toes began to tingle. She'd cry if she couldn't free them soon. Space Plumber cleared his throat. His gaze had shifted to her hands. She wiped her palms on her pants, then held her hands up for inspection. A heart line and a life line but otherwise empty.

A song from forever ago wafted from the ceiling. *"I want candy."* A children's chorus. When they got older, they'd see how little they needed.

Space Plumber studied her. "Didn't you forget something again?" he asked.

Were all godsends so nosey? She shook her purse; her keys jingled. The vouchers silent. The cash crammed tightly into her pocket. Her face was warm, the tips of her ears on fire. She had everything. Everything but the baby.

She closed her eyes, retraced her steps to the car, where she found him, strapped inside his seat. It was only March, the day a blue surprise, the kind you prayed for in February. How long had he sat there? A minute? Five? The sun was lukewarm. The temperature could only rise so high.

All but one of the numbered signs above the registers were dark. They'd closed their eyes to her. She drew in her breath. How long since she'd filled her lungs, saturated herself? She lived on little gulps of air that withered away before they opened the wings of her lungs. She needed more to accomplish this task. She sucked in all the air she occupied and her lips cracked as she opened her mouth and shouted, "Can't someone else open?" What every penitent wanted to know when the line stretched to the horizon. "My baby is in the car." Her throat throbbed. The tasks were many before she could get back to him. She cradled her head in her hands.

Someone pinched her elbow. She looked into Space Plumber's eyes. "Let me help you," he said. His grip was firm as he steered her to the customer service desk where the manager was waiting. A kind of miracle.

Space Plumber emptied her cart onto the counter, boxes and bags and bouncing apples. All the bar codes facing up.

The scanner bleeped. "Give me your SNAP card," the manager said. "And your WIC vouchers. Cash for the junk food."

She shook her head, like she was shaking the water out of her ear, clearing away the jumble of thoughts colliding in her brain. The car, the windows, the baby. She was losing the plot. When she looked backwards in time, she saw static, the fuzz of a broken signal. How could she find her way forward when the past was distorted?

She opened her bag. Keys, lip balm, crackers. Still no wallet. She wrestled with the envelope. Empty. All day she had thought the vouchers were with her and, despite all the trouble they caused – the lines, the questions – ready to fulfill their purpose. Like her wallet, they played a game of hide and seek. Now was not the time.

"I'll finish up here," Space Plumber said. "Go."

The manager glanced through the windows at the sun beating down on the cars.

Her throat was raw. Her toes ached. It was too much to thank him, too much to go.

She went.

Space Plumber's van threw a cool shadow across the car. The baby, asleep, his skin cool when she brushed his cheek. She had cracked a window. She had done it instinctively. Of course she had.

She was sitting on the stoop, a cigarette pursed between her fingers, when the school bus deposited the kids in front of the house. Kayla ran to her, huffing, a backpack swinging from her shoulders. She waved a piece of paper, a scrawl of numbers running down it. "I passed," she shouted. No one from school had called; no fists that day.

To celebrate, they strolled down the hill to the hotdog stand. Kayla read the menu posted between the take out windows. "Dog, dog, dog," she barked. Kayla and Kaleb ordered Michigans, the meaty sauce soaking into the roll. The baby bunched an empty hotdog roll in his hand. Kayla barked a thank you. The woman at the counter, ash on her forehead, scowled and shook her head.

Bonnie pressed her forehead to the glass. "Problem?" she asked.

The woman held out her big, broad hand.

Money. That was always the problem.

After the kids had gone to bed and the baby had fallen asleep, she swallowed the one pill she had saved, and she was warm and light and liquid. She could hear her mother scolding her, "This is how it starts." Her mother had risen every morning for work. Paid every bill. She had taught her discipline. It would be only one. The refrigerator hummed, sending mechanical messages to the other appliances. She took off her shoes. Her toes struggled against the tape, creatures with their own desires. She ripped off the tape, and her toes went to work, breaking the old blisters. She sat at the computer, called up a picture of her street, narrowing in on her block and her house, where she sat on the stoop in her jean shorts. The wind was blowing her hair up in twisted strands when the car with the camera rolled by, mapping her. She was talking to an invisible someone, one of the kids or their father who had no money to give her. What did he live on when he had nothing to share?

The phone rang, her ex's mother. "I saw what you posted," she said. "I'm taking you to court. You're going to lose that baby."

The baby wasn't lost. She knew just where he was. She retraced her day to find the thing that had offended the old cow but got stuck at the stoop, the surprising sun on her face, a pause in her wanderings, a figure at a rest stop.

Michael Horton

SWIMMING LESSONS

The sun spreads across the silt-brown water like melting butter. Wobbly strings of bubbles rise toward the surface. The boy's ears fill with water and silence. He hangs suspended. Alone. The panic and fear that possessed him when he was lifted in the air and flung out into the river – those feelings remain on the surface. Below in the silence, everything feels different, held in check. There is time. Time to decide to rise up through the bright yellow circle or go on hanging in the brown water. The broad slow slide of the river surrounds him. Silent but not still.

Matthew stretches his arms and legs out. Stretches them longer as if they've grown and he's finally the right size. Arms and legs spread out into a living X. X marks the spot. He is weightless. The water supports him. Holds him close, as close as he's ever been held.

He isn't afraid though he should be. It's like he's discovered a special place. A place where there are no expectations, no demands. A place he doesn't feel like he has fallen short again.

He can't see his father but imagines he can, standing on the lopsided gray dock jutting into the river behind their rental cabin. What

Michael Horton's work has appeared in *Glimmer Train, Iron Horse Literary Review, Raleigh Review, Whitefish Review*, and *Porter House Review*.

is his father thinking? Is he afraid for Matthew? Does he have second thoughts? If Matthew continues to hang in the slow drift of water, will his father dive in – disappointed?

No!

Matthew wants it to stay just the way it is.

It doesn't.

The urge to breathe bursts upon him. His lungs demand air. Arms sweep in panic, legs jerk and kick. The yellow light is too far away. Forever away. He reaches for it, reaches for it.

The light expands.

Arms flailing, eyes as wide as they have ever been, he breaks through the surface, sucks thin air and water into his open mouth. His thrashing spangles the river into chips of light. Overhead the sky pulses a shallow blue. On the dock his father, tall and lean and dark, is a silhouette in the sunlight.

Matthew swallows, gags, coughs. Water splashes into his eyes blurring his vision. His splashing fills the air. He can't breathe the water. Panic and the hot surge of shame flood through him. He is drowning.

Somehow, without knowing how, his head remains above water. Instinctively arms and legs are doing things by themselves, clawing and kicking furiously, thrashing the water as if fighting a tide. He moves against the slow current, not with it. He pushes against the water's density, pulls himself through it towards his father. There is a certain expectancy in the way his father stands on the dock, his stillness.

His father leans forward and sets his hands on his knees. Waiting. Because of the sun, because of the splashing, Matthew cannot see his face. The space around his father is too bright and his father too dark. He could be smiling. Matthew can't see, but he might be.

Above the wet furor of his own splashing, he hears the cabin's screen door slam. Matthew's little brother suddenly appears on the dock in his faded cartoon-print underwear. Jamie presses up against their father and stares out at Matthew.

Matthew sees his brother's bare arm encircle their father's leg. Their father glances down at Jamie's head, level with his hip. Matthew continues to churn in slow progress towards the dock.

Reaching it is like climbing to the top of a mountain. He flings a hand out, curls his fingers over the gray boards. With both hands, Matthew grasps the dock, pulls himself half out of the water, tilts his head far back to look at his father; an uncontrollable grin splits his face.

His father's expression is serious except for the lines beside his eyes. A keen observer of his father's feelings, Matthew believes his father's eyes are smiling.

Matthew's little brother is looking up at their father.

"Me," he says and tugs at their father's hand. "Me too."

Where Matthew is sandy-blond and thickset – *husky* had been the word his mother used, not fat – Jamie is dark-haired like their father and so thin and light Matthew can pick him up and carry him around easily. Younger by two years, Jamie wants to do everything Matthew does. Sometimes Matthew lets him follow him around. They play soldiers. Build forts. Sometimes Matthew tries to teach him what he knows.

"My turn," Jamie says. Their father looks down, both brothers looking up. Jamie is excited. No worry, no fear, no held-back tears, his face wide-open and eager.

Not Matthew. When his father asked if Matthew was ready, his father acted like it was all one to him. Matthew knew it wasn't. Sourness had surged in Matthew's throat and heat rushed to his face. He would not say he didn't want to – but Matthew didn't want to. Fear and shame muted him. He nodded his head.

Jamie – Jamie was just too little to know. He'd know better someday.

A trace of a smile pulls at their father's lips as he glances down at Jamie's upturned face. He shakes his head. But Jamie tugs at his hand. Their father puts his hand lightly on top of Jamie's head – Jamie, the one he says is his, through and through, no question about it. Matthew, he sometimes jokes, shaking his head, must be the mailman's.

Their father shakes his head again. It means something different this time. Matthew sees the wink. Slipping strong hands under Jamie's arms, their father lifts him up. Lifts him like he is hardly there. Matthew always feels like he is there.

"On three," their father says. He swings Jamie out, his feet sweeping over the river and back, out and back, and "Three!" He lets go. Jamie arches out over the river. Flying, weightless, the arc higher and longer than Matthew's. The river is as wide as the highway they'd driven on to get there. Our retreat in the woods, their father called it, standing and looking out the cabin's back door through the trees to the river.

Jamie hardly splashes.

Matthew stares where his brother disappears into the river. The surface smooths over almost immediately. A half-bubble like a soap bubble slides a moment on the surface then flicks out. Everything is quiet. Not the full silence Matthew heard suspended in the river, this is a poised silence, a held breath.

Matthew can no longer tell where Jamie had been thrown into the water. Can't tell he'd ever been there at all. He might not even have a brother.

A shadow passes over Matthew's head, the dark blue shadow of his father's body. A perfect dive, toes pointed. He enters the river without a splash.

Matthew grips the dock and the water buoys him. Above the sky is a shade of clear blue backed by infinite depths. Not knowing what will happen next but knowing something will, Matthew waits.

Jamie comes up. Up, up, up out of the water into the sunlight streaming strings of silver, lifted high by their father. He holds Jamie up like he is presenting him. Matthew's chest tightens. His eyes grow hot.

Jamie's eyes are wide – wide and blinking. He looks surprised. He coughs up water. Coughs and coughs. Their father holds Jamie high and walks in the neck-deep water to the dock where Matthew clings. He lowers Jamie and Jamie grabs hold of the dock next to Matthew. Their father leans forward, rests his hands on the edge of the dock, and lets his legs drift out behind him. The three of them float in the brown river holding onto the dock. Willow and river maple run along the banks, their leaves shiny and still.

His brother doesn't cry, only looks surprised. His face wide-open and surprised.

Matthew had been unable to hold back a scream.

Jamie bobs close beside Matthew. In their tiny apartment in the city they sleep in the same bed. Matthew always against the wall away from the edge. Before she disappeared – *flew the coop*, their father says, laughing short like he isn't mad – their mother tucked them in, read stories, kissed them each on the forehead. Mornings when Matthew wakes, he feels the tug on his hair. Every night in his sleep, Jamie twirls Matthew's hair into a knot around his finger. It doesn't really hurt. Matthew's hair comes loose easily when he pulls away.

Matthew stares hard at his brother floating between him and his father. Jamie blinks and blinks, like he's had a huge surprise. His mouth is open.

Looking at him a moment longer, Matthew's breath releases in a sigh. He lets go of the dock with one hand, reaches for his brother.

"You're too little," Matthew says, and understands it's true as he says it. The tightness in his chest opens. Holding the dock one-handed, he pats Jamie's shoulder so he knows he isn't being mean. "When you're bigger," he says, "when you're as big as me."

Matthew glances over Jamie's otter-slick dark hair. Their father looks beyond them both across the river into the trees. Whatever he is looking at, Matthew can't see it.

Matthew breathes in the river's breath, the smell of water, the heat of summer. He looks to the spot where he plunged through the surface. The river has erased it all.

When he looks back, Matthew feels glad. Glad his brother is saved, lifted aloft, sputtering and blinking. Glad his brother didn't drown.

And he's glad Jamie didn't learn to swim.

Matthew feels the water buoying him, buoying them all. Looking down at the surface, he sees a murky reflection of his face on the brown water and smiles but the reflection is wavery and unrecognizable. He looks over at Jamie then over to their father.

"You'll learn," he says to Jamie. "Just like me, you'll learn."

Marlin Barton

THROWING PUNCHES

1920

The boy worked the heavy bag and breathed in hot air laden with
the deep, rich smells of hay and horse feed. He was thirteen now and
stronger than he'd been last summer. He could feel the difference.
With each jab and punch, the bag swung a little farther. Not by much,
of course – they didn't call it a heavy bag for nothing – but enough
for Walton to come up and lean his body against the other side and
steady it. Or maybe Walton was just trying to make him feel good,
was only pretending the bag needed steadying.

"Nice," Walton said, and his praise made Conrad hit harder.
"Now try that very first combination I taught you."

The boy remembered. Left jab at nose level, another left to the
belly, right hook to the temple. His gloved fists landed solid every
time and sweat flew from his bare torso with each jarring.

"Remember, kill the body and the head goes with it," Walton said.
"All right. You been at it awhile. Want to take a break?"

Marlin Barton is the author of three novels, most recently *Children of Dust* (Regal House
Publishing, 2021), and three collections of short fiction. His stories have appeared in
The Southern Review, Shenandoah, The Sewanee Review, Best American Short Stories, and
Prize Stories: The O. Henry Awards.

Conrad grunted a *no*. He needed to keep hitting. Maybe just because it felt good, or maybe he was still angry with Walton and didn't know how to tell him. The man had showed up a week ago, a whole week, and hadn't looked for him once, had stayed holed up here at the Teclaw place with kin all that time. Maybe he'd already been working out himself inside this barn with the heavy bag hanging from a rafter, having forgotten all about last summer and his promise to teach Conrad more of the pugilist's art (which is what Walton sometimes called it) when he returned.

The boy didn't let up, kept working the bag with a series of straight right punches. Walton had told him early on that a straight punch had more strength in it, took less energy to throw than a hook or an uppercut. But each kind of punch had its place.

Walton finally backed away from the bag. "Stop. I don't have lighter gloves for bag work. I want to build your stamina, but your arms are getting tired. You're dropping your hands too low, leaving yourself open for a counterpunch. Remember, when you throw a punch you're aiming for the *back* of the head, right through the face. Then you want to imagine you're grabbing the end of a string and pulling it *straight* back, so your hand stays *up* where you can keep yourself protected."

"I know. I remember," he said and heard how his quick words sounded like jabs.

Walton looked at him and nodded, as if he understood more than what Conrad had said. "Let's get some water."

They both walked over to the bucket Walton had sat on a worktable earlier, after he'd drawn it up from the well outside the barn. Walton reached for the long-handled dipper and made sure it was full. "I'll hold it," he said, "so we don't have to take your gloves off."

Conrad lowered his mouth to the dipper and drank, and the angle of his head made him feel like he was bowing down to Walton, maybe asking forgiveness for his anger and rudeness that neither would openly acknowledge. He kept drinking and Walton turned the dipper up as he did, the way Conrad's mother might have done for him, or any woman with a child, and he suddenly felt embarrassed that a man was doing this. He was not used to a man doing things for him.

Walton filled the dipper again, drank for himself, and then lowered it back into the bucket and looked at Conrad. "I tell you what. Why don't we take off the gloves, after all?"

A part of Conrad wanted to keep punching, despite the June heat and the sweat that ran down his face and chest, but he gave in, wanted, on some level maybe, to be obedient to someone other than his mother. He raised his right, gloved hand, let Walton untie the laces and unwrap the strip of linen from where it was wound around his fingers, palm, and wrist. Then Conrad let him do the same with his left hand. He stretched both arms once the gloves were off, tried to loosen his tightened muscles.

"You've got a long reach," Walton said and sat down on a bale of hay and looked out the barn doors where the sun shone bright and sweltering. "Noticed your reach when I first saw you in front of the post office last summer."

Conrad leaned against the worktable. "You told me, that day. I remember." He paused for a moment. "So how come I didn't see you 'til this morning?" Walton turned back toward him as if he'd been waiting on the question. "Lyman told me a week ago he seen you. He was hanging around the depot after I left. Told me the next day, 'Your boxer man got off the train. Too bad he got beat.'"

He watched Walton carefully, wanted to judge how his words landed. Lyman *had* added that last part about getting beat, but Conrad knew he didn't have to repeat it. The man's expression remained unchanged, but his stillness seemed to deepen, to hold something within it he didn't want to let out.

Three months earlier he'd fought Jack Britton in New York, a city so big and far away from tiny Riverfield, Alabama, that Conrad could barely imagine it, as if the place was its own country across an ocean, where a tribe of people called Yankees lived. He and his mother owned no radio, no one in Riverfield did, expect for maybe a few crystal sets. He'd had to read about the fight several days later in the weekly paper out of Valhia, and his heart had broken for Walton, maybe as bad as when a girl breaks a boy's heart, but he didn't know about that yet.

"Ever need time to yourself," Walton finally said, "like maybe after your father died?"

Conrad knew Walton didn't want an answer, but he didn't know if you could really compare losing a fight to losing a father. Maybe you could.

"Eventually decided I couldn't keep staying to myself," Walton said. "Took the train from Memphis and come on down here. Knew my cousins would be expecting me. Maybe I came just out of habit."

"What about me?" Conrad said, unable to stop himself.

"I hadn't forgot you. But knew you'd want us to put the gloves on, and, well, let's say I didn't know if I could keep my hands from dropping."

Conrad wondered if he was referring to the fight with Britton, but he couldn't imagine Walton had lost because he'd dropped his hands.

He was a better fighter than that. Still, it had been bad for Walton. He'd read that Walton got knocked down in the second round, then again in the third, and they'd stopped the fight early in the fourth. The crowd had already been booing. He knew he had to risk bringing it up, felt like the longer he waited the harder it would be and the fight would feel like some ugly thing that kept them apart, like some lie one of them had told and neither would own up to it.

"You fought the welterweight champ," he said finally. "I mean, nobody beats Britton. You can fight him again."

Walton shook his head as if some great sadness had come upon him. "That won't happen."

"How come?"

"Not everybody gets a rematch. And if that sounds like a life lesson, maybe it is. Once you lose something, it's lost for good. I think maybe you know that already."

Conrad considered this, thought about the dead tone in Walton's voice, the quit in it, and wondered if there was something Walton wasn't telling him. "Well, I don't know why you *couldn't* fight him again. Seems like that's something you'd *want* to do, but it's not sounding like it."

Walton reached out the open palm of his right hand in a gesture that said *Leave it be*.

Conrad looked away from the hand and out the doors into the bright heat. "That why you hadn't seen me all week? Not because I'd want to put the gloves on but more because you knew I'd ask about the fight and you couldn't stand talking about it?"

"I reckon so. I guess you're a pretty smart boy."

Something in his answer, maybe that same dead tone, made Conrad feel disgusted with him. He didn't want to put the gloves back on now. Instead he cupped his hands, submerged them in the water bucket, and washed the sweat off his face and chest. Then he put his shirt back on.

"So are you done?" Walton asked.

Conrad walked toward the stall where he'd put up Jack, his pinto pony. "I reckon so," he said, echoing Walton's words intentionally. "About time for me to go home, anyway."

After he worked the bridle back on the pony, he led Jack from the stall and mounted him. Walton stood, watched as Conrad eased the pony toward the open doors. Then Walton reached out and caught Jack by the bridle, looked up at Conrad. "You want an explanation?"

"Of what?" Conrad asked.

"I didn't fight him well enough. I wouldn't be enough of a draw again. His management knows it and wouldn't ever want a rematch.

That was my shot." Walton looked down at the dirt floor, seemed to study the bits and pieces of hay strewn across it. "I would have been better off if I'd never fought him."

Conrad looked down at him. "Maybe you would have. You'd know better than me." He then pressed his heels into Jack's sides and rode out of the barn. ⟋

He kept Jack at a steady pace along the road that ran through cotton fields, and when he crossed over the pond dam, he looked back from where he'd come and admired the columns of the Teclaw house that sat in the middle of what had once been a plantation and was now farmed on shares. He didn't know exactly how Walton was related, but he knew Walton's middle name was Teclaw, and that Mrs. Amelia Reed, who Conrad's mother called, in suspect tone, the mistress of the mansion, had been a Teclaw. Conrad and his mother weren't poor, but she couldn't hide from him the struggle she'd been through since his father's death in '13. In fact, when she told him his father had died suddenly, he'd said, "Mama, first thing we got to do is count the money." He'd been six, yet already aware that life for them would be more difficult in a way that Walton's kin couldn't imagine, and he envied Walton having such a place to come to when he wanted to leave Memphis, and everything else, far behind. Maybe all the time Conrad had spent there last summer had been his own way of stepping outside of the life he usually lived: working at the depot most all of every day since dropping out of school in fifth grade, doing the hardest chores around the house for his mother, chopping wood, building all the fires every morning in winter, feeding the animals they owned, all the things a man would normally do.

Because he knew Jack was rested and watered, he kicked at his sides and gave him his head, ran him the last half mile until he was in sight of the old Stagecoach Inn. Up ahead he saw Lyman, who'd come out of the store where Conrad's mother worked and waited mostly on the women customers. He brought Jack to a stop as Lyman walked up. Conrad knew Lyman envied him his pony, and the fact that Conrad no longer had to stay cooped up in the red school house every day from after fall harvest up to spring planting.

"Where you been?" Lyman asked.

He knew Lyman could probably guess. "Up to see Walton."

"You put the gloves on?" The sun seemed to squint Lyman's blue eyes, but it was hard to tell for sure. Lyman always appeared squinted, not in a way that looked mean but, instead, nervous, which he seemed to realize and was always trying to hide.

"Yeah, I had them on, worked his heavy bag." Conrad had to check Jack who wanted to move on, knew his small pasture was near.

"Reckon he's got extra pairs of gloves?"

"I guess he does. Why?"

"I want to box you sometime."

Conrad looked away from him and up the road at the cluster of stores, past the post office and church, deciding what to say and how it might sound. "Lyman, you don't know nothing about boxing. Why you want to box me? I'll knock you out."

"Ain't you talking big." Lyman looked at him, his eyes almost closed. "I can handle myself." Then he added, with eyes wide open, as if he were about to make some important point and had to strain to do it, "My daddy taught me. I didn't have to go and ask nobody, like some loser I could name."

This was about what he expected of Lyman, was maybe why he'd talked ugly to Lyman first. He pulled hard on Jack, made him turn a tight circle around Lyman and came to a quick stop, hoping a hoof might come down on a foot. "Only person your daddy ever fought was your mama, and she laid him out with a stick of stove wood." He knew this was true. He'd overheard his mother telling it.

Lyman pushed at Jack's neck, tried to back him up a step. "Maybe I know something about your daddy that I could tell you."

"You don't know a damn thing, and if you say another word I'll beat you down right now."

Lyman looked like he was about to speak but then seemed to take the warning and stepped away, even as Conrad realized he *did* want to know what Lyman knew. He'd never fully understood how his father had died, knew his mother had never wanted to make it clear to him. Maybe Lyman knew something. "Just what *do* you know?" he said finally.

The squint-eyed boy appeared to study him. Then he shook his head. "I ain't gon' tell. Ain't my place." It was as if between telling and not telling he'd figured out what would aggravate Conrad the most. "Ask your mama," Lyman said.

Conrad aimed Jack toward home. "Don't worry, you'll get your wish."

"What wish is that?" Lyman asked.

"To see the back of your eyelids before you hit the ground." He shook the reins on Jack and left Lyman behind to puzzle out what that meant.

It was still light out enough for his mother not to have to burn the coal oil lamp in the middle of the kitchen table. So they ate in growing shadow but not dark. Her brown hair was pulled back, the way she wore it to work, and he could see she looked tired. She often did, her hazel eyes sometimes downcast into thought or sadness – he was never sure which. She'd asked if he'd unloaded freight this morning, he had, and if he'd had to deliver any telegrams, he hadn't, not today. She wanted to know if he'd split more stove wood for her and fed the chickens and the milk cow, slopped the two hogs. He had. Now he was waiting to find out if she knew about his going up to see Walton. He knew that, for some reason, she didn't like Walton, not that she'd ever said so exactly. It was just a feeling he'd gotten from her last summer after he'd spent so much time with the man.

"Saw you ride by the store this afternoon. You must have seen Lyman. He'd just left out with some penny candy. He told me that Walton was back, staying up at the Teclaws." She paused, looked at him. "Of course, I already knew that. Walton came in the store when he first got here."

He wanted to ask why she hadn't told him, but didn't. It was like her not to. Sometimes he felt she held so much back, collected so many secrets, that they all became a great weight inside her that she'd carry no matter how heavy they grew.

"That where you were all afternoon, up to see him?"

"Yes, ma'am," he said.

"Maybe he can teach you how to shoot this summer."

He didn't know what she was trying to get at. "You already taught me how to shoot."

"That's right. And how to fish and chop wood, and swing a hammer, even. Sorry I don't know anything about boxing. But I guess every boy needs to know how to fight."

"Yes, ma'am," he said. "But I could already fight, when I've had to. I wanted to learn how to box."

"Maybe you got that from your daddy," she said and seemed to look past him into shadow.

"Got what from him?"

"Fighting only when you have to. He was never one to start a quarrel. You're like him that way in your temperament, as best as I can tell. Or maybe I'm wrong."

He was proud to be compared to his father in any way, good or bad, truth be known. She'd told him before what a gentle-hearted man his father was, but she'd also told him, when he was eight, how his father once had to kill a man who tried to run him over with a horse. He'd wanted to collect on a bill the man owed at his store, and he'd been on foot when the man charged at him. His father had pulled a pistol and shot the man five times while the horse reared and reared again, finally riderless. After she'd told Conrad this story, she'd made clear the *only* reason she'd told it was so that he would not hear it from someone else who might want to paint his father in a bad light. He wondered now if this was what Lyman had wanted to tell him about, and to tell it in such a way as to insult his father's memory.

Whatever it was that Lyman had hinted at kept worrying him more and more, and he knew now that he had to tell his mother about it, to see what she might have to say.

At first she remained silent as the room seemed to grow darker. "Sounds like that boy's on his way to being as sorry as his daddy," she said finally.

"Think he was going to tell me about Daddy shooting that man?"

She pushed her plate away, half a piece of cornbread still on it. "Probably so," she said, but her words came too quickly, it seemed, and she had not looked at him when she spoke them, still did not look his way but instead at the window behind him, as if she could see some memory through its panes.

He wanted to push further, to see if she might offer any other thought about what Lyman could know, but he realized it would do no good. Then a different kind of question came to him, one he'd never thought to ask. "Was it hard on him?"

"What's that?" she said, almost absentmindedly, as if she wasn't fully aware of his presence.

"Was killing that man hard on Daddy?"

Now she looked at him with such surprise, seemed to see him as a stranger almost. "You've never asked me that, but yes, son. It was hard on him, in all kinds of ways. And he'd lost his brother Henry not too long before. Guilt and grief will take a toll on anybody, especially a man like your father."

He had more questions, wanted to ask what kind of toll, and what she meant by a "man like your father," but another look at her downcast eyes slowed him, and then she rose from the table in a way that told him their talk about his father had ended.

The train from Valhia built up steam and finally pulled away from the platform, its couplings jerking each car forward with a hard clangor and enough power to cut a man's hand off if caught inside those metal parts. The train was headed toward Demarville and from there on to Meridian and Jackson, cities he'd never seen but liked to imagine. Larger cities, such as Chicago and New York, places where Walton had fought, seemed mostly beyond his imagination. The freight he'd just unloaded with a hand truck and had stacked up on the platform was real enough, though. He could still feel each crate in his hands and arms and lower back, and in the sweat on his face. Most of it was dry goods for store owners, and since the day was not overcast, he could let it sit until it was picked up. Now he'd carry the mailbag up to the post office. Mr. Traeger, who managed the depot for the L&N Railroad, hadn't trusted him with it at first, had been reluctant to hire him to begin with, but finally had said, "I'll do it for Phil's sake, though I know he wouldn't have wanted you working so young."

Just as Conrad carried the mailbag out the front doors, where Jack waited tied to a rail, Walton took the first step up toward him, his hair combed wet, still.

"What you doing here?" Conrad asked. "You need to send a telegram?"

"No, I borrowed Amelia's car." Conrad saw the Model T parked at an angle. "Figured I'd come see you a minute."

"I'm carrying the mail up to the post office."

"You want a ride?"

Conrad came on down the steps, passed Walton. "No, don't need one." He threw the mailbag across Jack's neck, looped the strap over the saddle horn.

"How about I walk with you?"

Conrad untied the reins and swung himself onto Jack, turned toward Walton. "Fine with me. I'll try to keep him at a slow pace – if I can." Walton seemed to find something mildly humorous in this, as if Conrad had told a joke and didn't realize it.

"You seemed put out with me when you left yesterday. Want you to know I'd like for you to come up much as you can this summer." Conrad could tell from the sound of Walton's steps that he was having to quicken his stride. "I'll work with you again. We can do some light sparring, more than we did last summer. It'll be good for you."

"What about you?"

Walton was quiet at first, as if he didn't understand the question, or maybe needed to think about his answer. "Let's just say it'll give me something to do."

Conrad pulled back lightly on the reins, so lightly he hoped Walton wouldn't notice, and he looked sideways at the man. "That all? Just something to do? You not going to keep yourself in training?"

Again, Walton was quiet a moment. "I don't know. Only so much training I can do here, anyway, without experienced sparring partners. And I don't have a fight coming up."

Conrad nudged his heels against Jack. A part of him wanted to make Walton trot, or even run. Conrad knew he was young, but he didn't like being dismissed so out of hand as a sparring partner for Walton. "So no fight coming up," he said, and then added, in a low voice, "Got any left in you?" The sound of Jack's hooves, and Walton's steps, may have muffled his words enough so that Walton couldn't have heard them. He wasn't sure, and Walton didn't let on if he had heard.

They approached the main road, the Methodist church and the cemetery where Conrad's father was buried directly in front of them, Conrad and his mother's house not too far to the right hand side of it. They turned in the opposite direction toward the post office.

"So how about it?" Walton said. "You gon' come up, keep putting the gloves on?"

The sun was at ten o'clock now, the road through town brightly lit, the heat of the day coming on. "You got extra pairs of gloves? Lyman thinks he wants to box me, and I know I want to knock him out."

"Why would you want to do that? Isn't he your friend?"

"Don't every boxer want to knock out the other man? Besides, he started to talk bad about my father, and he called you a loser."

"You already told me as much about what Lyman said." Walton caught Jack's bridle, stopped him short, and looked up at Conrad. "Sometimes boys say things they don't really mean."

"And sometimes they say mean things."

Walton kept his gaze on Conrad. "I know that for sure."

The soft, quiet way Walton had spoken made Conrad want to turn away, and he felt a kind of burning in his eyes that lasted only a moment.

They were now passing in front of the store where his mother worked, a store his father's father had once owned, and across the street sat his father's old wooden store, vacant now. His mother had said maybe one day he would own and run it, be a proper merchant.

"I'm gon' stop and say hello to Louise while you go to the post office," Walton said. "Come in when you're done."

It struck him as odd to hear Walton call his mother by her first name instead of saying "your mother," sounded too familiar, and he knew it would be best if Walton didn't go in, but he only nodded.

He rode on around to the back of the post office, took the mail inside, and spoke to Mr. Penniwit, the postmaster, a small, bandy-legged man whose age Conrad couldn't guess. The man turned from the chicken-wire partition stretched across the front counter and lowered his glasses. "You looking more and more like your daddy, boy."

"Thank you," he said.

For a moment it seemed like Penniwit was going to say more but then thought better of it, as if maybe the similarity between Conrad and his father didn't bode well for the son and shouldn't be commented upon further. Conrad dropped the mailbag and picked up the empty one from the day before.

When he rode back around to the front of the store, Walton was already standing on the porch, Conrad's mother beside him. It looked as if she had just spoken to Walton and that he didn't know how to answer her, or maybe didn't want to answer her.

"You're not going to let Walton here ride behind you, are you? Might be too much on ole Jack," she said.

"No, he walked alongside me from the depot. He can walk back."

Walton stepped off the porch, started away from them without a word, which seemed a kind of answer to whatever his mother might have said to him a moment ago.

"See you this evening, Mama." Conrad watched her shake her head, wondered why, and then he turned his pony, caught up to Walton. When they were a little farther away, he said, "I don't think she likes you." If it hadn't been so obvious he wouldn't have said it.

"No, I don't think she does. Mothers can be peculiar sometimes, have their own way of seeing things men can't fathom. But it's all right. Don't hold it against her."

They turned onto the depot road and entered again the canopy of tree limbs that offered protection from the sun's heat. "What exactly did she say to you? I know it was something."

Walton stopped, and Conrad pulled up on Jack's reins, waited for an answer. Walton kept standing there, making him wait even longer. "She thinks I'm teaching you to be violent," he said finally, as if it had taken him that long to remember.

"*That's* what she said?" He shook his head. "That don't sound like her."

Walton looked away, then back at him, but not all the way, not in the eye. "All right, maybe I shouldn't say this, but she told me I'm not your father, that I shouldn't try to be."

The words landed less like a punch and more like an illegal jab, one he didn't see coming, but he wasn't sure why they had a sting to them. He knew Walton wasn't his father. So why did he feel so embarrassed now, ashamed almost? It was as if his mother, who was so good at keeping secrets, had told one on him that she couldn't have known, had maybe made up. He hadn't even wanted to see Walton earlier, would just as well have ridden off without him.

"I know you're not my father."

"I know that, too," Walton said, and the words seemed to come so easily to him.

There was that sting again, though not as strong, just enough to confirm what he'd already felt. He quickened Jack's stride and then had to keep himself from turning to see how far behind Walton was, if he'd picked up the pace of his steps.

When Conrad rode up in front of the depot, he saw someone bent over looking into Amelia Teclaw's Model T. As soon as the figure turned around he recognized Lyman, who squinted at him as if the sun were in his eyes. Conrad dismounted Jack and tied him to the rail. Then Lyman walked toward him, and he saw Walton slowly approaching the both of them.

"What you doing, Lyman?" Conrad said.

"Guess I come to see if you were around."

"How come?"

Lyman only shrugged. Maybe he didn't know. He often came to the depot. Maybe he'd come out of habit. Maybe he was lonesome. Conrad didn't want to stay mad at him, but he wasn't ready to forgive the day before, either. Whatever Lyman knew about Conrad's father, he still knew it.

Walton came up and leaned against the side of the car, greeted Lyman. "I hear you're wanting to box Conrad."

"Yes, sir. I am."

Walton slowly shook his head. "I don't know if that's a good idea. Wouldn't really be a fair fight," he said, and Conrad felt a sense of pride at hearing the words. Then Walton looked at him and Conrad knew Walton could see the pride he felt. "Afraid you two boys going to end up fighting no matter what I say, with or without gloves. I don't want to see that happen." Walton turned from one to the other of them, and Conrad knew something else was coming, that some notion had taken hold of Walton, something Conrad might not like. He didn't know how he knew. He just did. "Lyman," Walton said, "if you can make your way up to the house the next few mornings, or if maybe I come get you, I'll give you some lessons."

Conrad had no words to say, not even *betrayal* because the hurt he felt came quicker than any one word could.

Walton must have seen his blank face and known what was behind it. "Only fair. You need to understand that, Conrad. I don't want anyone to have too big an advantage." Then he turned to Lyman. "Well, what about it?"

"Yes, sir. Thank you." Lyman seemed so shocked by the offer he had trouble getting the words out.

"So it's 'sir' now?" Conrad said. "That sure ain't what you was calling him yesterday."

"Conrad," Walton said, probably guessing at and so interrupting what Conrad was about to say, "you can still come up any afternoon you want, or can."

"If I *don't* come, maybe you can give Lyman here some extra lessons."

Walton worked his jaw a moment, as if it held tobacco. "That would be fair, would let him catch up to you a little more, but no, we'll keep right along. Long as you want."

Both Walton and Lyman were looking at him now, waiting to see what he might say, but he didn't say anything at all, not a word. He looked toward the depot doors, hoping maybe Mr. Traeger was wondering why he wasn't back yet and would come out and call to him. He didn't. "I got to get back to work," he said finally and then turned and walked away from them and toward the heavy doors.

That evening his mother commented on how quiet he was, and if she suspected it had anything to do with Walton, she didn't ask. After they ate, and before dark, he walked alone down in the small pasture and along the creek he sometimes fished for bream. Because the house was so hot inside in the summer, he and his mother always sat on the front porch until bedtime and would call out to and talk with whoever happened to pass. Tonight, just before good dark, a Black man everyone knew as Moon, because he made liquor, came by in a wagon. He called out first and they answered. Then, after night had come full on, a car flew past, headlights boring through the dark, and the smell of dust quickly filled the air. Conrad couldn't help but breathe it in and then tasted the fine, sour particles in his mouth.

The next afternoon he had to deliver two telegrams, one to the farthest point on Loop Road and the other to the Caulfield place on the Tennahpush River. So he couldn't have gone to see Walton even if he'd wanted. As he rode Jack and delivered the telegrams, he felt an ache in his arms, something pent up that went deeper than his extremities, a pang inside that only solid-landing punches would remedy. But what he most wanted was to hurt Walton in some way, and he knew he couldn't do that physically.

After leaving work the next two days he went directly home and fed the animals and did his other chores. He decided he'd just stay away from Walton, completely, would let him teach Lyman as long as they wanted. He'd simply ignore the both of them, let all of Walton's teaching and Lyman's sweat come to nothing.

Late in the week he went fishing on the creek but grew restless. Finally he caught four bream, enough for his and his mother's supper. After cleaning them and leaving them in a pan on the kitchen counter, he headed to the front porch to water the plants like his mother had asked and he'd almost forgotten. As soon as he let the screen door slam behind him he saw Lyman standing at the gate and realized he was disappointed it wasn't Walton. It was clear from the way Lyman stood leaning against a post that he'd been there for some time, waiting. He didn't want Lyman coming up onto the porch, so he walked out, without speaking, and met him at the gate.

Although Lyman stood in the shade, his eyes looked narrowed by the sun. "Walton says you ain't been coming to see him." He spoke slowly, carefully, with what sounded like a kind of confidence Conrad didn't expect. When he looked again, he saw Lyman's blue eyes opened, and they appeared a darker blue than Conrad remembered. "He's wondering if you ain't gon' come no more."

Conrad looked up the empty road toward the stores and post office. "Did he ask you to come talk to me?"

"No, and he didn't *tell* me he was wondering about you, either. I could just see it, and been wondering myself."

Just as Conrad was disappointed it hadn't been Walton standing at the gate, he realized now he was disappointed that Walton *hadn't* sent Lyman. "So what y'all been working on?"

Lyman pushed away from the gate post, stood a little straighter. "What you'd expect. He's showed me the right kind of stance, how to throw a punch the right way. Showed me some combinations."

Conrad looked directly at him again. "I figured your daddy showed you all that already. I thought you said he'd taught you how to fight, that you didn't need a loser to teach you." He paused a moment, and then said, "So who's the loser?"

Lyman kept his eyes on him but didn't speak. It was as if he needed time to decide how to answer in a way that would do the most damage.

"Tell Walton I ain't coming up there no more. And Lyman, I ain't gon' fight you."

"How come? Don't be like that." He couldn't tell if Lyman was disappointed or angry. It almost sounded as if he were desperate to prove something to someone, to anyone. "He's just teaching me a little of what you know, but *I'm* still willing to fight. How come you ain't? You afraid? And what you mean, 'So who's the loser?'"

"I ain't afraid. Just don't feel like it no more. And who's the loser? Is it not Walton anymore? Or is it your daddy who you know good and well ain't never taught you nothing."

Now Lyman's eyes were bulging, and he struck the post with an open palm. "My daddy ain't no loser. Yours was a drunk, and he drank himself to death. *That's* what I didn't tell you the other day."

Conrad wanted to punch him over the top of the gate, then bust through it, shove Lyman onto the ground and punch him in the mouth until his lips broke open, but some cold part of himself took hold, stopped him, as if whatever he'd learned of the pugilist's art had made him more calculated, maybe even mean in a studied way that he'd no inkling of before now.

"Get out of here, Lyman. And you best keep taking your lessons. You gon' need them."

Lyman nodded, maybe knew it was best for him to keep quiet. He slowly turned away and headed up the road toward the stores, and Conrad heard a car approaching from the other direction, could tell it was moving fast, maybe was the same car as the other night, cars being so rare. It flew past again, a stranger behind the wheel, and now the dust rose, surrounded him, and he watched Lyman mostly disappear into the same roiling cloud and then reappear a little farther along as if the cloud had carried him and left Conrad standing still.

He was drawing water up from the well behind the house when he heard his mother open the door of the screened-in back porch and walk down the first few steps. He turned and watched her sit on the third stair from the top as she often did when she got home from the store. She still wore the light blue dress from this morning but had let down her hair, and even though he knew how long it was, she wore it up so much that when she loosened it the length always surprised him, as if he were abruptly seeing some younger version of her from a time before he was born, was maybe seeing her as his father once had.

She was looking past him now, down toward the creek, and he wondered if that's what she saw or if some memory filled her gaze. He took the water bucket and went and sat beside her, some part of him wanting her attention but another wanting to see what she saw.

"Thanks for carrying the water," she said. "Maybe later I'll get you to fill the reservoir on the stove. Might be a night for a bath."

He didn't know if she meant a bath for him or for herself and didn't ask. He realized he'd sat beside her not so much to see what she saw, or even merely for her attention, but to hear her answers to the questions he hated to ask but knew he'd have to as soon as Lyman had said those words about his father. He forced himself now, pushed his own words out, and knew they'd come as something of a shock to her. "Was my daddy a drunk? Is that how he died?"

She let out a lengthy sigh, filled with the sound of a weary breath and maybe a kind of relief, as if these were questions she'd expected he'd ask one day and she would finally have to rise to them as best she could. Then she wasted no more time in answering. "He was not a drunk. And whiskey did not kill him. You need to know those things, you hear?" She turned toward him then so that her knee touched his, and he felt both the pressure of it and the comfort in the touch. "In his last years he drank in a way he hadn't before. He'd lost his brother, Henry, and his father died not too long after. Then he had to kill that man. All that changed him." She placed a hand upon his back now, as if her touch there might be more intimate and might ease him and help him understand. "He stayed gentle, though, never let alcohol turn him mean, like it does some, like the father of a boy you might know. He never drank early in the day, and there were weeks, even months, he didn't drink at all. Most of the time when he did drink you could not tell it. He rarely ever slurred a single word. Sometimes it took – got the best of him. But he didn't die because of it. The day he died, he'd drunk some, but not enough to kill him." She stopped a moment as if she were trying to recall the day and struggling against it. "*Something* made him sick. I don't know what. I took him to the doctor in town, and the doctor gave him a shot. Some claim it was the shot that killed him, but Dr. Hamblin was too good a doctor, and your father was better when we left. No matter what somebody else might name, it was grief and guilt that killed him, not alcohol. Whiskey makes some men sorry creatures." She paused, maybe trying to find the right words. "Your father was *always* a good man. He was never sorry. *That's* what you need to know."

Conrad looked down into the water bucket between his feet, glimpsed his reflection and then saw past it and, just for a moment, saw in memory his father walking through the front gate and toward the house, smiling at seeing his son standing on the porch next to his mother. Then he was climbing the steps and beginning to speak, but Conrad could not hear or now could not remember what he was saying. And then he disappeared into the ripple of Conrad's reflection as a breeze stirred the water's surface.

He believed all his mother had just told him, felt the truth of it inside himself, yet knew how she could keep to herself what she didn't want you to know, and he wondered if she were doing that now, not lying, just holding back. He would have to trust what she *did* say – and what he needed to believe.

"So why ask me these things now?" she said. "Did somebody talk badly about your daddy? Maybe a boy I could name?"

He found he didn't want to answer, felt the need to hold back something of his own.

She waited and did not push, and when he remained quiet, she looked at him and smiled as if she'd just seen how much he was indeed her son. He felt maybe she was even proud of him for his silence.

The next afternoon, as he rode Jack across the dam and looked up toward the big house, he wondered if Walton saw him approaching. He'd been hesitant to come, but now that he was close, he realized again how much he wanted to see Walton. He'd been mad at him before, but it hadn't kept him away. He wanted to urge Jack along but kept him at a steady gait.

When he reached the yard in front of the house he saw Aiken, one of Amelia Reed's grown sons, sitting on the wide porch in his rolling chair, crippled from the day he was born. "Never know which of you boys gon' turn up here," he said. He grinned and showed his large, square teeth that made Conrad think of a mule chewing briars, set as they were in a strong jaw so at odds with his paralyzed body.

"Walton here?" Conrad asked, still atop Jack.

"He walked around back a little while ago."

Conrad nodded a thanks, nudged Jack forward. Once he passed the side of the house he found Walton leaned over the well housing. The man then straightened and turned, as if he'd sensed Conrad, had been waiting on him even, but the look on Walton's face surprised him. He appeared worried, his mind preoccupied. Or maybe it was Conrad who was worried that what he saw in Walton was something akin to disappointment that was aimed his way.

Conrad tried to make a joke. "You wishing at the well?"

Walton only shook his head. "Just wanted to feel the cool air coming up. What I would've wished for already didn't happen."

He knew Walton must mean losing the fight, or, rather, winning it.

Walton turned away for a moment, then back toward him, and Conrad felt as if Walton were looking at someone else, not a boy on a pony but someone grown he needed to explain himself to. "Maybe I should have wished beforehand just to go the distance. I got greedy, wanting to win. I knew he was a better fighter. If I'd fought him a different way, I might've gone the distance, and maybe had a shot at the end. I played it wrong."

Walton didn't sound quite like himself, and this wasn't the first time, but today he sounded even less like the man he'd been last summer, and Conrad wondered how often he played the fight over in his head. And for how long now? Months it would be. He missed the man he'd gotten to know last summer, maybe in the same kind of way he missed his father.

"I want to put the gloves on," Conrad said. "I want to fight Lyman."

Walton moved toward him. "You've changed your mind again. How come?"

Conrad checked Jack, kept him still. "It don't matter how come. I just want to. Besides, you probably already know. I figure Lyman's told you."

Walton didn't reply one way or the other. He only began to walk toward the barn in measured steps. Conrad put his heels to Jack, came alongside Walton, who finally looked over at him. "You're not wanting to box him. What you're wanting is to knock him out – cold, I imagine."

"Maybe."

"That can be dangerous."

They entered the barn and Conrad dismounted, put Jack in a stall and tended to him. He then noticed the three sets of gloves on the table and took off his shirt, hung it on a nearby peg.

Walton picked up a pair of the gloves. "These are yours. They been waiting on you." He pitched them to Conrad. Then he tore strips of linen off a roll, had Conrad sit down on a hay bale, and wrapped his fingers, palms, and wrists. Once he finished, he pulled the gloves onto Conrad's hands and tied them. Walton was leaned close to him, their faces near, and for a moment Conrad remembered when his mother would pull on his mittens for him on cold days when he was young, something his father hadn't done.

"Should have gotten us some water," Walton said. "I'll get it later. Right now I guess you need to work the bag for a while."

Conrad stood, approached it, stretched his arms and flexed his fingers inside the gloves. He was ready to hit, felt the need of it.

"You might throw some jabs," Walton said. "Then maybe start with that first combination you learned and go through some of the others, if you remember them all."

Conrad did as he was told, though he didn't feel as though Walton had really *told* him to do anything. His jabs landed solid, and he could feel his blood quicken and rise. Then he threw a left jab at nose level, another to the belly, and a hard right hook to the temple.

"Good enough," Walton said. "Now maybe the jab and straight right." Somehow Walton's directions were sounding more like afterthoughts and less like real instructions, as if he were too busy thinking about the punches he'd thrown, and hadn't thrown, against Britton.

Conrad landed the jab, then threw a hard right. Then again and again, harder and faster each time.

"Go to another combination," Walton said and Conrad wondered if he was really watching or if he'd decided he had better give some kind of different direction, no matter how random.

He threw a left jab at jaw level, then the same right, and when his weight shifted with the straight right, he followed with a left hook low to the body.

"Guess you haven't forgotten anything. Better keep those hands up."

"I practiced all year. Shadow boxing, so I *wouldn't* forget." Sweat was now running down his chest and the smells of hay and feed were filling his lungs, making him feel like some work animal, which he didn't mind, maybe liked.

"Well, good for you."

Walton's tone made him want to hit harder than ever. He went quick to a left jab, a straight right, followed fast by a left hook and another right. Each punch landing well and the bag moved in a way that was satisfying and made him feel strong, somehow larger than his frame. Even his reach felt longer. He wondered if Walton was now seeing how well he hit.

"Getting pretty hot in here. I best go ahead to the well," Walton said and began walking toward the open doors.

Conrad let fly with every combination he'd just thrown, wanted Walton to hear and maybe even feel the jarring of each punch. The man had never walked away from him like this when he was working the bag, and he couldn't believe Walton was doing it now. Go to your damn wishing well, he thought. Wish for what didn't happen. Wish yourself away.

He kept at it, felt his hands dropping, and worked to keep them raised. Finally he stopped and took deep breaths. Then Walton came in with the water bucket and set it on the table and got a drink for himself. "You need water?" he asked.

Conrad shook his head *no*, but of course he did.

Walton took several swallows from the dipper and put it down. "You need to spar," he said. "We haven't done that since last summer."

"That's why I come up here." He paused a moment. "You sparred with Lyman?"

Walton took off his shirt – Conrad saw the hard chest, the flat stomach – and sat down on the bale Conrad had been on earlier and began wrapping a hand with linen. "We've sparred a little. It's only fair." He then gave a quiet, short laugh that didn't really sound like a laugh. It was more as if he were responding to some private joke on himself.

"What?" Conrad said, wondering if instead the joke was on *him*.

"Nothing really. Just realized I'm sparring with boys these days instead of men."

Conrad wiped the sweat from his cheek with the back of a glove. "Must be a real comedown for you."

"Didn't mean it quite that way. I didn't."

How did you mean it, then? Conrad wanted to ask. He pounded the ends of his gloves together so that they pushed down more snuggly on his tightened knuckles.

Walton picked up a pair of gloves that were already tied and pulled them on. "Don't have head gear for us. Most boxers spar with it now. Of course I'm not going to hit you hard, especially in the mouth. Just hard enough to let you know you been hit. You can hit me a little harder. Some might tell you different, certain sportswriters I could name, but I can still take a punch." Walton stood, let out a breath. "Well, maybe I can."

"I'm not exactly Jack Britton," Conrad said and saw Walton flinch just slightly at the sound of the name, maybe no more than a twitch below an eye, but it was visible. Conrad wondered if Walton's having the gloves on made the fight come back to him stronger.

"We'll spar in here, like before," Walton said. "I'm starting to feel a decent cross breeze with these doors open."

Conrad met him in the middle of the aisle, all the stalls on either side empty, save the one with Jack, their only spectator. They touched gloves, backed up a few steps, and Conrad moved into his stance, his blood rising again and his breath a little short, but he knew the tension he felt good, needed. He wanted to be the aggressor, knew from last summer that Walton would wait, force him to move in. So he did, threw a jab that Walton blocked and followed with a straight right, which didn't land either.

"Stop already," Walton said. "That's too predictable. That's the first combination most people learn, and it's why I started you with that jab-straight-hook. Don't be predictable."

"That how you started Lyman?"

Walton shook his head, probably meaning no, but also that he couldn't believe Conrad would ask such a question. "Started him with something different. But it's nothing you haven't learned for yourself. I'm not looking to give either one of you an advantage."

Conrad raised his fists, began moving toward Walton again and watched as Walton tucked his chin and anchored his right hand against it. Conrad threw a left hook that didn't land solid and was about to follow with a straight right but realized he'd let it drop a little, and that's when Walton popped him with a left jab and just as he did Conrad knew what was coming, remembered too late Walton's pulley punch. As the man drew back his left, his straight right was already springing forward, as if the two hands were operated by a pulley, and the right struck Conrad square on the chin, hard enough to stun.

"Sorry," Walton said and dropped both hands to his side. "Hit you a little harder than I meant. You all right?"

"Yeah, fine," he said, not sure if he was angry at Walton or more angry with himself for leaving himself open.

"Well, you've got to be able to take a punch."

"I know that," he said, each word a jab. He moved in quick now, wanting to take Walton by surprise. He threw jabs and then leaned in, put his head against Walton's chest, right under his chin, could feel and smell Walton's slick sweat, and began throwing more jabs at his body. Walton would know what he was trying to do, and when Walton lowered his head down to eye level, he was playing along, ready to sacrifice himself. Conrad pushed him away then and threw the uppercut Walton had to be expecting, landed it square on Walton's jaw, hard enough to make him grunt. Conrad didn't let up, moved in close again, and when he did he felt his left foot land atop Walton's left and knew how off-balance he was now, tried to recover quickly but Walton's straight right caught him above the ear, not hard, but hard enough, and Conrad knew he was falling even before the fall began, suddenly nothing but air beneath him and no purchase, and then he was down in the dirt, on his side with an elbow dug into the rotting pieces of hay and looking up at Walton, whose face appeared pained.

"I hated to do that, son."

Conrad was angrier now, more than before, but he heard that last word, knew it was just a word, one that men used sometimes when talking to a boy, though Walton never had until now. Maybe it didn't mean all that much, or anything at all, but he heard it, kept hearing it somehow, as if it were an echo repeating from a separate time, its source another voice he had not heard in years. He scrambled to his feet finally, stood before Walton, and could not have said if it was anger or memory that made him feel such pressure in the corners of his eyes.

"Take a few deep breaths," Walton said, looking close into Conrad's face. "I didn't knock you out. We both know that, okay? You were off-balance, and you're mad at yourself right now. Because you remember what I talked to you about last summer. If an opponent ever missteps, gets thrown off-balance, always be ready. He's wide open. You want to throw the right punch and throw it hard. There's nothing dirty about it. I want you to remember that and use it to *your* advantage."

Conrad found he could not speak, was afraid of what would happen to him if he did, and so nodded instead.

"Don't get disgusted with yourself. That won't help at all. Believe me, I know."

Conrad felt a cross breeze cool the sweat on his face and heard Jack bumping against his stall door.

"We're not done yet," Walton said, "but I know you need water. So sit down. Just imagine we're between rounds. We'll get back to it in a few minutes."

Conrad did as he was told, and felt like he was being told. Walton took the bucket by the bail and set it at Conrad's feet. He reached for the dipper and though it was clumsy to handle with his gloves still on, he found he was grateful that Walton had not held the dipper for him as he'd done before. Maybe Walton knew such an offer by a hand that had just knocked him down would have been too misplaced for what he needed at the moment.

That night on the porch, he waited until good dark to tell her. He would not have been able to if she'd been looking at him in clear light, and even when it first turned dark he didn't know if he could. She sat in the swing, its chain creaking slightly as she pushed against the porch boards with her toe. He sat in a ladder-back chair near a front window.

"I thought I'd forgotten the sound of it," he said and briefly paused, bit his lip, "but I heard Daddy's voice today."

At first his mother was quiet, as if she were now listening for this father's voice too, was waiting for it to apprise her of something. "How'd you come to hear him?"

"I just did," he said, not wanting to explain, but he had already told her where he'd gone after working at the depot.

"What did he say?"

"He called my name. That was all." It was a small lie, but he again felt the need to withhold, to keep something for himself, and he knew better than to tell her Walton had called him *son* and that his father's voice had spoken out of that word.

The swing was still now, no more creaking sound. "Was it a comfort to you?"

"He sounded like hisself, the way I remembered and didn't think I could. So I reckon it was," he said, though he hadn't been sure what to make of Walton using the word he had, and he'd been angry at the time, so maybe it hadn't been any comfort.

"Can you hear him now?" she said, her voice coming out of the darkness almost like it had no real source.

"No, not right now."

"Well, since you've heard it again, maybe you'll hear it more, and you can keep hold of the sound of it, not let it go. I hear him all the time."

"You do?"

"He talks to me, tells me how to handle things. I can hear him so plain sometimes."

He leaned forward in his chair, toward her, as if he needed to so she'd be able to hear him because he knew he was about to speak in a lowered voice and ask something he knew he shouldn't but had to anyway, and even though he was certain how she would answer, he felt some great need to hear it again, needed to hear the certainty, no matter how clumsy his attempt to prompt her and no matter how angry she might sound. "When he talks to you," he said and then hesitated, gripped the seat of his chair, "does he ever slur his words?"

He could hear her move against the swing and toward him, was afraid she was about to stand over him. Maybe he wanted that. "Son, why would you ask me that? I told you your father was not a drunk and you better remember that, never ask me such a question again. Did you not believe me before?"

"I believed you," he managed to say, not sure if it was true.

"Then why ask that?"

He didn't know how to answer and gripped the seat of his chair even tighter. "I'm fixing to fight Lyman tomorrow," he said finally, or blurted out, rather, as if it were some kind of answer to her question. "I mean I'm going to box him," he added, though this was not further explanation of anything, and he felt he was making no sense to her or to himself.

"You want to fight him?"

"Yes, ma'am. I want to."

"He been talking about your father again? That why you want to fight him?"

"Yes, ma'am."

"Or do you just want to fight because you think you know how, now that Walton's taught you all the finer points?"

"Maybe that, too."

She settled back in the swing but then remained still. "Walton going to be there when y'all fight?"

"Yes, ma'am."

"Maybe you're wanting to fight because he'll be watching."

He didn't answer but wondered if she was right. Maybe that was a part of it.

"Well, if you're going to do this," she said and then paused for a moment, was maybe leaning forward again, "make your daddy proud of you."

Her words struck him strangely, almost as if she meant *make Walton proud*. Again, he didn't respond. He heard a car drawing near, headed toward town and traveling not fast this time but at a steady speed. He could not yet see its lights and found himself waiting on them.

He showed at the depot just before lunch, and while Conrad hadn't been expecting him, he was not surprised when Lyman appeared on the platform beside the tracks. He knew Mr. Traeger didn't want Lyman hanging around inside the depot, so Conrad went out to him, broom in hand as if he needed to sweep. It was a familiar object, felt good in his hands, was comforting in its way.

"You looking for me," Conrad said, "or do you got long-lost relatives coming on the next train?"

"Just needed somewhere to go." Lyman looked around as if searching for something. "Walton come by this morning," he said finally.

"Did he? By your house?"

"Yeah. He usually carries me up to the Teclaw place. He said you was ready."

"I am. It's time."

Lyman looked down at where the broom rested on the platform, seemed to stare at it, and kept staring at it, as if he wanted to hold it himself, or wanted something already claimed by another that he could take up in his empty hands. "Daddy didn't come home last night," he said and didn't look up, as if he'd had no intention of saying what he did and was suddenly far too embarrassed to face Conrad both by the fact of what he'd said and that he'd admitted it to someone.

Conrad pushed the broom a few inches to the side and found he didn't want to answer with anything mean exactly but needed to say something, maybe just to get him past his own embarrassment at what he'd heard.

"Neither did my father," he said, and though his words came out harder than he'd intended, when Lyman looked up at him with his wide-open eyes, Lyman only nodded as if he understood something that had just passed between them, and then Lyman seemed as though he might say more. Conrad knew you couldn't compare a father who'd died and would *never* come home again with one who'd been gone only one night, but as he held Lyman's gaze the difference didn't make him angry, though he couldn't have said why it didn't.

When Conrad rode past the house he saw no one on the wide porch, and if he had he probably wouldn't have asked if Walton were around, would have simply rode on directly to the barn, which he did now. What he saw there, and didn't see, surprised him. Neither Walton nor Lyman were waiting, but there were ropes pulled across the aisle and tied to posts, and on each side other ropes ran parallel, giving shape to a makeshift ring with what looked like two old milking stools just outside opposite corners, folded towels on top of each. He put Jack in a stall, saw the gloves on the table, and took a drink of water that tasted fresh. He didn't sit, had too much restless energy. Instead he stepped into the ring, walked to its center and took his stance, began to throw quick punches and combinations, but they did not calm him. His stomach felt tight.

After throwing several more jabs at an imaginary figure, he realized he'd been hearing voices for a few moments before they registered. "Good that you're loosening up," Walton said. Conrad stopped, turned to face him, and saw Lyman. "Went to pick him up," Walton said. "Planned to be back before you got here. We got delayed a little," he added and looked at Lyman as if there were something unspoken between them. Conrad wondered if Lyman's father had come home yet, or where the father might be. Did Lyman know? Had Lyman maybe kept that to himself earlier, couldn't quite say it?

Conrad stepped out of the ring. "Is it regulation?"

Walton took hold of the top rope. "Not quite, but close enough. And you can see, there's no tension in the ropes. Nothing exactly professional here, and we won't go past four rounds, if that much. When I stop y'all, that's it. Same thing if one of you goes down."

Conrad nodded. He hadn't thought about how long they would fight. He looked over at Lyman, who remained quiet, seemed distracted. Conrad didn't feel angry at him now, but still found he wanted to fight, maybe for those reasons his mother had named. The tightness in his stomach grew, and he needed to *move*, his restlessness rising to meet his need.

Walton looked at both of them, seemed resigned to something. "Well, y'all get those shirts off and wrap your hands. I'll check the job you've done before we get the gloves on."

Conrad sat on one end of the hay bale where he usually sat and began winding the linen around his left hand. Lyman took the other end of the bale. They kept their backs to each other, and Lyman still didn't speak to him. When Conrad looked over his shoulder, he saw how straight Lyman sat, his back rigid, his muscles tensed. He seemed angry about something, something that must have happened since Conrad had seen him earlier. Maybe his father had come home and there'd been trouble.

Walton looked at Conrad's hands and slipped his glove on for him, tied each one, then did the same for Lyman. "Y'all both stand up," he said, and there was something grave in his voice, as if he knew whatever might happen, good or bad, would be his fault. He looked again from one to the other of them. "Y'all are both feeling it. I can tell. Remember, you're not trying to kill each other. You're friends. But this isn't sparring, either. It's a fight."

Lyman finally stole a glance at him, and Conrad saw his eyes looked wet, determined, enough so that he knew he better be ready, had best be on the attack at the outset.

"Y'all get in the ring," Walton said, and Conrad noticed he kept speaking to both of them at once, as if he didn't want to show favor to either. But he'd known Walton longer, had learned more from him, had talked to him more and spent more time with him. He couldn't help but think Walton wanted to see him win. If he didn't, Walton might feel like he hadn't taught him well, had failed him. He wanted to show the man he could *box*, and wanted to show he had a knockout punch.

He followed Walton to the ring, watched him place the water bucket at a corner, and stepped into the ring before Walton did. He turned when he reached center and saw Lyman and Walton approach. Walton held a silver pocket watch in his left hand, and Lyman stared past him, out the far doors and seemingly at nothing. A cross breeze blew through and it was only when his wet skin cooled that Conrad realized how hot the air felt and how much he was already sweating.

"I'm referee and timekeeper," Walton said. "Three minutes for each round. In between we'll break long enough for me to give each of you water, and advice. Fight clean. I didn't teach either of you any different." He and Lyman both nodded at Walton in acknowledgement. "Come up and touch gloves. Then step back a few paces. When I say *start*, commence."

Lyman held out his gloves, looked at him with squinted eyes, and he touched his gloves to Lyman's, stepped back and Lyman seemed to disappear. He no longer saw him, not his wet, squinted eyes, not the boy with a no-good daddy, only someone he had to punch and bring down or else suffer in the failure just as Walton had.

Then he heard the word *start*, heard its sharpness, and came forth.

Lyman seemed to wait on him with hands raised and ready. Conrad moved close, bobbing his head as he did, and threw a left jab at Lyman's chin, then another, the second one landing well enough, and he felt himself settle down but still remained beyond alert, followed with a right hook when Lyman left himself open, landing it well, too, but Lyman took it, got his hands back up, and threw a straight right that fell far short and Conrad realized what a difference his long reach made. He could throw from a farther distance, stay out of Lyman's way, but still he found himself wanting to move in close and did now, surprised at how well he could *see* the fight, both Lyman and himself, and threw the left jab at nose level, another to the stomach, was two punches into the combination that was second nature to him, pulled back to throw the right hook and felt the jar and sting below his left eye when Lyman slammed him with a right and then moved in, tucked his head against Conrad's chest and pushed off, landed the right uppercut that Conrad knew was coming, but he took it, felt he had waded *into* the fight now, was not angry but instead determined and focused in a way he'd never been. This wasn't life or death but it felt like it was. *Kill the body and the head goes with it* ran through his head. He stepped back, got his hands up, and when Lyman came at him, surprising him, he blocked the punches and landed jabs and uppercuts into Lyman's ribs and stomach, one hard blow after another and knew they hurt. Finally Lyman tried to clinch him, and this time he put his head against Lyman's chest, pushed off, and hit him with another uppercut. Lyman went to clinch him again and Conrad then became conscious of Walton for the first time when he separated them, stood between them for a moment, and then got out of the way. Now Lyman kept his distance, threw punches that fell short as Conrad kept his left extended, pushing at Lyman's head whenever Lyman tried to get just close enough. It was as if neither could now decide how to fight the other. A stalemate began to settle in with the two of them facing each other and moving in a slow circle around an unmarked center, but Conrad knew that was no way to fight, and he moved toward Lyman for more punches to the body, saw Lyman crouch, head forward, and was about to throw a straight right at Lyman's forehead when he heard the sharpness of *stop* yelled loud and had never been more surprised by any word or sound in his life.

Walton looked at him and pointed to a corner, then pointed at the opposite corner from Lyman. "Y'all take seats," he said.

Conrad walked over, realized how heavy he was breathing, inhaling the same old smells of hay and animal feed as sweat poured from his body. He grabbed the stool and sat, watched Walton towel the sweat off Lyman's face, head, and shoulders, then gave him water and talked to him in a low voice as he leaned down toward him.

Now Walton came to Conrad carrying the bucket and wiped him down. "You each get one piece of advice," he said as he held and tilted the dipper. "Here's yours. Use your reach. Don't fight him close."

Walton moved toward the middle of the ring, looked at his pocket watch, and after just a few seconds shouted *start*. Conrad rose, could feel the water had done him good, and realized almost too slowly that Lyman wasn't waiting on him this time but came at a charge, and Conrad was just agile enough to sidestep the punch Lyman threw, felt the *whoosh* of air as his fist sailed past, and before Lyman could recover Conrad threw a right hook that landed more solid than any punch he'd ever thrown at the heavy bag or at Walton and the thrill of it charged through his body, the current traveling up his arm and into his chest and stomach and even into his head so that for the blink of a moment he did not see what was before him, but Lyman failed to take the advantage, could not have known he'd even had it. Then Conrad saw he couldn't have known because he was still shaking off the punch, which is when Conrad realized it was a punch that should have taken him down, and would have most anyone their age, and wondered why it hadn't. Was Lyman tougher than he thought, or had something *made* him tougher just for this one day, something that had filled him all through the afternoon? He knew then he'd lost his focus, could have followed with a hard left and done with it what he hadn't with the right, but now Lyman was up against him, pouring sweat, too close for him to throw a knockout punch, their acrid scents merged into the breath of their bodies, and the moment he felt Lyman's uppercut that he stupidly hadn't been ready for, he knew Lyman had recovered, at least enough where the fight was not near over, like it had become its own animal that the two of them fed through sweat and tensed muscle and some shared need neither would quit pursuing, as if each punch was the only answer either of them knew to give to a question they didn't understand, and they were no different than any boy, with or without a father, who'd ever come before them. The fury of adrenaline took him now, had them both, and they answered blows to the body one by one, jabs and uppercuts rebutted with grunts until Walton once again edged between them, had to push them away, but they hadn't been clinched, there'd been no call for separating them, but he'd done it and they had obeyed. Conrad got his hands raised again, watched Lyman do the same, and then glanced at Walton who checked his pocket watch, lowered it, looked at them both and yelled *stop*. Conrad stood in place, arms at his side, and when Walton looked at him again and pointed to the corner, he went reluctantly and knew his disgust showed.

Walton came to him first this time, gave him water. He took several swallows and then was able to speak. "You stopped the round too soon."

"No, I didn't." Walton wiped Conrad's face with the towel. "That's not something I'd ever do."

"But you did. I know it."

"Trust me. I didn't. When you fight, time disappears. I checked the watch. Now quit arguing and listen. Stop fighting him close. That's the only way he can fight you. Stop giving him his fight."

"You tell him to fight me close?"

Walton looked at him with what was maybe his own disgust and covered Conrad's head and face with the towel before walking away with the water bucket.

He took deep breaths, pulled the towel off, and watched Walton see to Lyman and speak close in his ear. Then Walton moved out into the ring again, checked his watch and called *start*.

Lyman approached and he reached out his left hand again, keeping Lyman at a distance, throwing short jabs as he could, waiting to set up a hard straight right. Maybe when the chance to use his right didn't come quick enough he got frustrated, or maybe his anger at Walton drove him toward disobedience. He moved in close, worked Lyman's body, took punches from Lyman, and then stepped backward just far enough and pulled his right hand back, anchored it to his chin, daring Lyman to close in and throw a punch, and when he did, if he dropped his hands too low, Conrad would show he could throw that pulley punch too, just like Walton, hit with the left and, while pulling it back, throw the right at the same time and rotate his hips into it, take Lyman out. But Lyman didn't take the dare and Conrad closed on him, stepped in for an upper cut, but knew the second he did it was wrong, couldn't believe the reckless error he'd made, and only hoped he could get his left foot off of Lyman's before Lyman could react, if Lyman even knew how to, but Conrad had already dropped his hands, reaching for balance that was just beyond him, and what he caught was Lyman's right hook against his temple that sent him sideways and the time between falling and landing disappeared into nothing a silver pocket watch could measure – no watch could show a half second lost to blackness that the jarring of the ground took away and left one only stunned but awake again.

He scrambled up, tried to hide how unsteady he was on his legs, but Walton was already staring him in the face and his *stop* registered. "That's it, like I told both of you," Walton said.

"But I'm up. He got lucky 'cause I stepped on his foot. He didn't knock me out. Let us keep going. If this was a real fight, we could."

"No." Walton put a firm hand on his shoulder, looked at him with a level stare. "If one of you went down, I said I'd stop the fight."

"It was nothing but a lucky punch. I'm fine."

Walton shook his head and looked over at Lyman whose arms were at his sides. He wasn't smiling exactly but appeared victorious nonetheless, something like pride welling up into his blue eyes, stolen pride, Conrad thought. "It wasn't lucky," Walton said and looked again at Lyman. When he did, Conrad felt some small piece of knowledge enter his mind and couldn't believe the truth of it.

"You told him," he said.

"Told him what?"

A hot breeze blew down the length of the aisle and offered no relief from the heat.

"To be on the lookout for it," he said and watched Walton pretend sudden understanding.

"No, I didn't. And you hush. Stop thinking that right now." He looked over at Lyman and back at Conrad. "Wait a minute," he said. "Just wait. This is between us. Lyman, let me untie those gloves. Then I want you to take the bucket out to the well and get some of that cool water and wash yourself off." He began with Lyman's gloves, and Conrad could only discount the look of mild confusion on Lyman's face. "We'll be out there directly. Go ahead."

Lyman nodded. "All right," he said and walked out the open doors, carrying the bucket in his still linen-wrapped right hand, which made him appear wounded, though Conrad couldn't imagine why since he'd just been declared winner.

He began trying to pull off his right glove now. "You told him how to take me out if I stepped on his foot. Told him I might do that, 'cause I did it last summer and did it again yesterday. I can't believe you."

"No, I didn't." Walton reached for and pulled at the laces on his glove. "When I saw how bad you wanted to knock Lyman out and told you that could be dangerous, I meant for you, that it could make you careless. Why would you think I'd do such a thing as tell him your biggest weakness?"

The word *weakness* surprised him, felt like a blow to a vulnerable spot, an already bruised rib. "I think it 'cause I know you ended that round early just like you separated us when we weren't even clinched and I had the upper hand. But mostly 'cause you want me to be like you."

"How's that?" Walton untied the left glove now but did not look away from Conrad for one moment.

"You're so ate up 'cause you lost that fight you wanted me to lose too. That's how. You been feeling sorry for yourself, acting like a loser. Lyman was right when he called you that, but he got to win, 'cause of you."

"You're a boy, Conrad. And you can't help that. So you don't know what a man my age goes through when he sees his only chance for something he's worked so hard for slip away. I'd lost a few fights, but this one was something else, something more than a fight. And the way I lost was shameful, embarrassing. It took a toll on me. You're right about that, but for you to think I'd turn on you because of my failure is wrong-headed. But you're embarrassed too right now. So maybe I can understand why you want to think that way."

Conrad was suddenly aware how dry his mouth was now, dry enough almost to steal his tongue and any words he might say, but Walton had let Lyman carry the water away like he'd earned it, like it was his prize, and hadn't thought about what Conrad needed. "You gave him the fight and even gave him the damn water."

"I didn't give him anything, and we'll get water in a few minutes. What I *did* do was to try to help two boys who I thought needed help and might appreciate it."

"We ain't no charity cases, and you ain't our daddy."

Conrad saw the look of surprise on Walton's face, heard him say, "No, I never thought I was, not for a moment," and felt again as if he'd taken a blow to a bruised rib, only this time he hadn't known the rib was bruised and vulnerable. And now he couldn't speak, felt only confusion and no way to express it, found what he most wanted was the clarity of a combination, imagined slamming Walton with a straight right, a left hook, and another straight right, imagined the satisfaction each punch might deliver, then heard, from somewhere in his flawed memory, the sound of his father's voice, but he couldn't hear the words or even if his father was calling his name, and then it was gone and all he was left with was a longing for what he'd had and lost that was maybe as strong as Walton's for what he'd wanted. But still he couldn't speak, could not make sense of all he felt.

"Could be I was wrong to train the two of you," Walton said. "Maybe that was disloyal to you, and maybe I failed to be what you wanted – I'm thinking now I did – but you would have had such an advantage, and that boy didn't need to be beat down. Besides, you were winning the fight, and would have won. But learning how to lose is important too."

"Guess you know all about that now. You're an expert."

Walton closed his eyes, shook his head, and didn't respond. Then he turned away, looked like he might walk out of the barn, and Conrad felt dismissed, like a schoolboy a teacher gives up on and the rest of the class knows it. After another moment Walton did begin walking away, but when he reached the open doors, was right at the edge of hard sunlight, he faced Conrad again. "You need water. Come on with me."

Conrad followed but kept quiet, decided anything he might say would be wrong, or too hard for him to say. He began unwrapping the linen from around his right hand as he walked. When he caught up with Walton he looked ahead and saw the bucket sitting on the ground beside the well. What he didn't see was Lyman, only the two strips of linen piled near the bucket.

"Where do you think he went?" Conrad asked as the two of them kept moving. "Inside the house?"

"No. His shirt's still in the barn. He wouldn't have gone in the house without it, or wearing it, either, for that matter."

Conrad bent down and reached for the dipper, took a drink, and even though the water was now warm he drank again. "You think he left? Heard us talking?"

Walton looked in several directions. "Probably so. I'll go and pick him up."

"He won. Strange he'd just walk off."

Walton faced him but didn't speak at first. "His father's in jail. Maybe I shouldn't tell you that."

"For what?"

"I've said enough. And don't repeat what I've told you, even when you hear people talking about it."

Conrad nodded, knew he might hear his mother bring it up, and she would ask him if he won the fight. He wasn't sure how he would answer, what part he might keep for himself.

Walton looked down at the bucket, picked it up, and touched a finger to the water. He poured it out and brought up more from the well. "Now drink," he said.

Conrad did, and then, without thinking about it, said, "I'll see to him. You don't have to go."

He watched Walton stand there quietly, the sun bright and painful on his face, his hands hanging at his sides at the end of a reach that was longer than Conrad had ever considered.

Alyson Mosquera Dutemple

THREE-SEASON ROOM

Outside, the November air pinches, but it's warm on the screened-in porch where Shelly and Charlotte are getting high. They pass the joint back and forth between them as they would have back in high school, had they been friends. But Shelly and Charlotte are not friends. They're sisters – not the same thing. This, despite a needle-point their mother hung in the house where they grew up that claimed, "A sister is a friend for life." Their mother had three sisters herself and died while not on speaking terms with any of them. For a long time now, Charlotte suspects that sister-love is really just a proximity thing.

Because she is high, she is moved to share this thought.

"What's that supposed to mean?" Shelly rasps, craning her neck to face Charlotte. The two of them are lying flat on their backs, head to head, like murder-suicide victims or conjoined twins. They have discovered that the artificial turf on the porch feels pleasantly springy if you lie on it long enough. When Shelly looks at Charlotte from such a close range, Charlotte sees tiny broken capillaries on Shelly's nose

Alyson Mosquera Dutemple's work has appeared in *Colorado Review, Passages North, DIAGRAM, The Journal*, and *Wigleaf*.

and the places where her sad-mom mascara has migrated into her wrinkles. Charlotte blinks her own naked lashes, thinks suddenly, and with some alarm, that Shelly looks not just like an *older* sister, but an *old* one. Does this mean Charlotte is old too?

"I don't know what that's supposed to mean," Shelly repeats. "Of course, we're friends. Of course, we like each other. We *love* each other. I mean, think of how we were joined at the hip when we were young."

"Were we?" Charlotte asks, genuinely surprised, and also a little touched by this information.

Shelly grabs the joint from Charlotte. "You smoke too much of this stuff," she says. Charlotte watches thin fingers of smoke wind themselves from Shelly's frown lines when she exhales. The windows are closed on the porch where they lie, the room Shelly calls her "three-season" one, so the smoke is trapped inside along with them.

Sometimes when Shelly exhales, Charlotte imagines her own lungs squeezing and contracting, as if they really did share some of the same body parts. And when Shelly's son, Henry, comes calling after a nightmare, "Mommy! Mommy, where are you?" Shelly sighs, stubs out the joint, but Charlotte is the one who has to stop herself from answering.

Smoking weed used to put Charlotte to sleep, but these days, it, like everything else, leaves her wired, restless. Late into the night, she stays awake in her nephew's tiny bedroom, all the things she owns in this world, her laundry, her insurance paperwork, her knives, taking up one small space between the toy box and the closet door. The bed on which she sleeps butts up against a wall shared by the master bedroom, where nothing of interest ever goes on between her sister and her husband, except for hushed talk about Charlotte herself.

"It's not me I'm thinking about, but the kids," her brother-in-law Darren says, when he thinks that he can speak freely, when he thinks Charlotte cannot hear. "They need to get back to normal. To their routine. I have no problem with your sister or her lifestyle. To each his own, I say. But, how long do her problems have to be our problems? Yesterday, Henry asked me if gangrene was hereditary."

There is a pause. Charlotte strains to hear Shelly's reply. The words come out mumbled, as if spoken from a head over which a pillow is being held. "She's not even looking for an apartment anymore," continues Darren. "I checked the browser on the laptop. You know what she's been doing all day? Watching cooking videos on YouTube. I bet she hasn't even called a realtor."

Charlotte makes a mental note to call a realtor tomorrow, first thing! She pauses the video she has been watching on her nephew Henry's bed. The screen freezes on a close-up of a knife, the skillful hand that operates it just out of frame, blocked from Charlotte's view. Charlotte imagines holding the knife herself. She squeezes her palm around the handle, but her palm isn't there.

Charlotte prefers the word maimed to injured, or incapacitated. She has had nearly a year to settle on this word choice. As in, the car accident *maimed* Charlotte. It *maimed* Charlotte, but killed Raul, Raul being Charlotte's fiancé, his car being the one she wrapped around the tree.

Since the accident, Charlotte no longer has use of her right arm. She cannot feel a thing below the shoulder. She has been told that beneath her skin, the "muscle is dying." She likes to imagine this phrase giving her goosebumps, but only on one side. Two corrective surgeries, so far, have not proven so corrective. Nerves are fickle things, her surgeon says. They are delicate circuits, difficult to rewire. We will try again, he says. We will try again.

Each time the doctor broke the news that the surgery didn't take, he looked so sorry, but so clean, and Charlotte thought to herself, Where is the blood? Where is the gore?

She knows she should be feeling something else after the surgeries, but all she can muster is curiosity.

Charlotte suspects that if she had not been the one driving that night, Darren probably wouldn't be trying to kick her out. Likewise, if she had been the one who died, there would be no reason to get rid of her because she would already be gone.

The accident report called Charlotte's driving "reckless," but Charlotte feels as if it has not been reckless enough. Instead of grief, there is only obligation. She now feels as if she owes Raul a debt that she cannot pay. She has outlived him by 212 days, 31 Saturdays, and 84 dinner services at the restaurant where they met and where each of them no longer works, for obvious reasons. Her debts keep racking up. She counts them, measures them out while in her nephew's bed, her dying arm propped up next to her on its own pillow, like an uninterested bedfellow.

When Charlotte moved in with Shelly and her family, her nephew Henry was made to move across the hall to accommodate her. He now sleeps in his big sister Dalia's room. Henry doesn't mind Charlotte living in his space, but even so, Charlotte has given the children a hermit crab for their troubles. Dalia is afraid of the thing, but Henry is quite fond of it. When she handed over the tank the day she moved in, he exclaimed, "Now you can stay in my room forever!" and Charlotte thought it strange that the price of her forever was a small terrarium with a plastic tiki hut in it.

Henry's room is tiny, his walls covered with posters of NASCAR drivers, all of whose statistics and biographical information Henry can recite at will. The sheets on which Charlotte sleeps are decorated with tracks on which racecars zoom all night long in a never-ending circuit. When she falls asleep Charlotte dreams of engines, figure eights.

In the marital chamber next door, a monotonous sound of waves eventually drowns out the conversation, and Charlotte can no longer eavesdrop. She shuts the laptop and places it on the floor. She arranges her arm on its pillow, allowing herself to fondle the wrist of it for a dull moment. She closes her eyes, concentrates on a pulse. In the darkness, a voice cuts the silence. Darren exclaims, "You've got to try harder, dammit!"

Charlotte knows he is talking to Shelly, his wife, but she squeezes her own wrist tighter. Feeling nothing. More nothing. Then less than nothing at all.

* * *

The surgeon who her sister sees has prescribed her medical marijuana because Charlotte has had trouble sleeping ever since the accident. And because the weed is prescribed by a doctor, Shelly can't see any reason to take issue with it. She has no problem with Charlotte smoking on her property after the kids go to sleep. She has no problem even sitting beside her sister in the quiet of the three-season room, keeping her company, like a candy-striper. And when Charlotte offers to share a little with Shelly one night, Shelly is surprised that she also has no problem saying at once, "Well, maybe a little."

Unlike Charlotte, Shelly has not smoked a lot in her life, but lately she is beginning to think it's not too late to fix that! She discovers she likes it. Likes even the fact that she likes it. Charlotte's prescription has given her something unexpected to look forward to. At odd moments during the day, braiding Dalia's hair, zipping Henry into his winter coat, Shelly finds herself anticipating these forays onto the porch with her sister, the earthy smell of the joints, the burn in her throat. These are not, she thinks, the joints she remembers passing up at college parties, lip-wet, limp, reeking of b.o.

No, these joints are something else entirely. They call to mind for Shelly a tea she once drank at a temple in Japan. That summer during college. A million years ago. The tea, as she remembers it, was served in earthenware mugs without any handles. To drink it, you had to wrap both hands around the vessel, hugging the warmth all the way to your mouth.

"You know what this room needs?" Shelly asks Charlotte one night as they lie head to head on the turf, the smell of the tea wafting around her. "A fountain."

Shelly pulls her phone from her pocket and with a few focused swipes of her finger, she locates and orders a "moderately priced Zen-water garden" to keep in the three-season room along with them. This, Shelly thinks, is just the thing.

The very next day, a package arrives. It is smallish, but surprisingly heavy.

"What's that?" Henry asks, as Shelly makes straight, shallow incisions into packing tape.

"A fountain."

"For wishes?"

"No," Shelly says, thinking, maybe, sort of. She opens the box and pulls the Zen-water garden out amid an explosion of packing peanuts. Shelly stands the thing on the counter to study it. Henry comes up beside her, placing the hermit crab whose shell he had been painting next to it. The word "NASCAR" drips off the crab and leaves a smudge on the basin it rubs against. "Yep," Henry says, appraisingly. "It's a fountain, alright."

That night, Shelly carries the moderately-priced Zen-water garden past the living room, where Dalia and a homely friend of hers watch television. The two girls stare solemnly at the screen on which Humphrey Bogart appears to be mumbling. Shelly doesn't know what film it is they are watching. It may be, she considers, *The Maltese Falcon*, one of many movies Shelly regrets never having seen. There is too much! she thinks, hurrying past them. Too much never something or other.

Around midnight, after the kids are asleep, Shelly sets up the fountain on the porch. She pours a pitcher of cold water into its basin and turns it on with the flip of a switch. Charlotte chortles, blowing smoke through her nose, when the fountain begins to bubble. It sounds like an old man pissing, she says. But Shelly likes the noise of it, the tiny tinkle, the sound of an itch being scratched.

"Why don't you say something in Japanese," Charlotte says drowsily after some time spent alternately listening to, and laughing at, the fountain.

Shelly combs the folds of her mind, trying to locate a word, any word, that she had learned on her trip. But her mind is slow, and that summer, so long ago. Any Japanese she had once known has been lost, scattered to time. Loose change pulled from pockets before going into the wash. The only word she can come up with is one that she learned from watching a cooking show on YouTube with Charlotte.

"Umami," says Shelly.

Charlotte laughs as if Shelly has told a joke. But Shelly finds herself repeating the word, as she once used to do when reciting meditation mantras. Though she has given up meditating years ago, she misses the feeling it gave her, like closing your eyes while you're still awake. "Umami," she says to the porch roof. Long ago, when Charlotte was still a chef, and Raul still alive, she had told Shelly that chopping up vegetables into very small, even pieces felt like meditation to her. Shelly thinks suddenly, maybe I should get a knife! Maybe I should try to make things smaller.

That Shelly smokes pot with Charlotte isn't the point, says Darren, though it's true he doesn't approve of it. The point is that Charlotte is still here at all.

"What did you and your sister do together all day?" he asks tersely from the walk-in closet as he undresses at night. When he asks this, he snaps off his tie like a whip. Shelly likes this small, defiant gesture. It makes Darren seem meaner, and thus, somehow more appealing.

"Are you stoned?" Darren always seems to want to know. It is a word that Shelly has never considered. Especially as Darren likes to say it. In his mouth the word sounds strange, biblical.

"Real nice, Shel. Real mature. And with your kids in the house. Classy."

Darren turns on the white noise machine app when he is done with her. Fed-up, disgusted. Shelly lies awake and listens to the waves from the app crash, dredging up each ghost of other arguments, earlier arguments. The room grows thick with ghosts. Shelly once had a friend who described her marriage as "rocky." At the time, Shelly didn't understand the term. But now she thinks she does.

"I just want life to go back to the way it used to be," Darren says occasionally into the darkness.

"Me too," says Shelly. And she means it when she says it. Just not the same life, maybe. Not the same way, perhaps.

When Darren gropes for her body beneath the sheets, Shelly makes herself count to ten before shooing his hands away.

"I'm trying," Shelly lies earnestly, pulling down her nightshirt.

"I need you to try harder!" says Darren.

Shelly thinks her problem is that she has become too impressionable. Soft like sand. Her body, once so taut and responsive, is now shifting, untrustworthy. Shelly frets a lot about something Charlotte has told her. How splinters of glass can emerge from the skin of an accident victim, months, years later. How they can just pop up through the surface out of the clear blue, painfully, and just when you thought there were no more. Shelly lies awake and worries that something might be waiting to break through her own skin, though she herself has never been injured. Other times she worries that there is nothing down there. Nothing at all to relieve the pressure.

When Shelly sleeps, the waves do not come from Darren's white noise, but rather from the Sea of Japan. In her dreams, she stands on the edge of a great pattern of raked lines in the sands of a meditative garden, her body entwined around a beautiful young man's. The man is the tour guide on the trip with whom Shelly fell intensely, aerobically, in love that summer during college. He was 27 at the time. A baby! Shelly thinks now. And yet, it hadn't seemed so then. Now, she feels old enough to be his mother.

Before Shelly started smoking with Charlotte, Shelly hadn't thought about the tour guide, the boy, for a long, long time. So long that now when she thinks of him again, dreams of him, she isn't sure if she is remembering things she has done with him or things that she wished she had done with him. They both seem equally impossible, the things her body did and the things she wished it did. The lack of distinction between the two make Shelly's memories, even the most carnal among them, feel as if they belong to someone else and she is just borrowing them temporarily.

Shelly supposes that the return of these dreams of the tour guide should bring her happiness, but they do not. Instead, the dreams leave her dazed, frustrated. For a long time after she wakes, she looks at the tissues in Darren's wastebasket, at the children's fraying toothbrushes in puddles by the sink, as if she has never seen any of these things before in her life. She looks at her own skin in the mirror but cannot bring herself to touch it.

Some people only discover religion after their children are born. But Shelly has done the opposite. Her children are secularists. They have called her attention away from what she used to worship. She used to fall asleep meditating on memories of lines made with rakes, of the boy with his fingers, of traced patterns on soft surfaces. The life she has now does not accommodate such a practice. It is full of stuff and loudness, crab claws clacking over gravel, fabric ripped from the teeth of a zipper. All day long, her family obligations buzz around her brain, occupying every lane of her thoughts, the children, Henry and Dalia, jockeying for space like racecars on the circuits Henry watches, each trip around her mind re-writing any memories of Shelly's that preceded them until, eventually, Shelly feels as if her life must have only begun the moment they were born. That any part of the life that came before them wasn't real. It couldn't have been. Well, could it?

Only now, Shelly has become the owner of a moderately priced Zen-water garden that dribbles softly in her three-season room. Now, Shelly has proof that she was once concerned with more than this thundering life.

Shelly closes her eyes, plunges her hand into the cold water of the fountain and lets it sit there grazing the stones and rocks near the filter at the bottom until a biting sensation causes her to recoil, to pull her hand back, and cradle it against her body. Maybe the bracing cold. Maybe something sharp down there.

* * *

Dalia's summer had royally sucked. She had wanted a dog, but she got a hermit crab. She was supposed to go to a wedding, but instead she went to a funeral. Since Aunt Char moved in with her family, and Henry moved into her bedroom, nothing has been right.

"That does suck," Dalia's friend, Cass, whispers cross-legged on the floor of Dalia's closet where they sit. They have to shut themselves up to talk in there so as not to wake Henry as he sleeps in the bed. "It sucks capital-D dick."

Dalia nods, appreciating Cass's willingness to "go there" with her curse words. Cass is widely considered to be crass by the other members of the 6th grade. Cass *is* crass, actually, always talking to Dalia about things Dalia secretly finds distasteful, her collection of photographs from nature magazines of animals "doing it," for example. But for all her faults, Cass appreciates what Dalia considers her Dalia-ness, her big teeth, her bad attitude, her frizzy hair that she still needs her mother's help to tame, and for this Dalia is grateful.

"What does Char stand for anyway?" Cass asks, picking at an ingrown toe nail.

"Charlotte."

"Well, it sounds like a cut of meat to me," whispers Cass, flicking the freed nail into a pile of clothes that have slipped from their hangers. "Some rotten old burnt piece of meat."

"Aunt meat," says Dalia, agreeably. "Aunt Dead Meat."

The worst of it, as far as Dalia is concerned, is that Aunt Charlotte just can't seem to understand that she is not wanted here. That Dalia, especially, doesn't want her. She doesn't want to hear her voice, or see her face, or have to get a glimpse of that dead thing that hangs off her body.

"Hey, Dally!" Aunt Charlotte says brightly whenever Dalia enters a room, but Dalia always pretends she cannot hear. She has started to wear headphones everywhere now, even inside the house. She likes the force-field of silence they project around her, even when they are not turned on. They protect her from her pathetic aunt. Dalia moves about the kitchen, opening the refrigerator, packing up her book bag in the morning, while her aunt's mouth forms words that Dalia ignores. Her aunt is just a mouth to her with no sound coming out. A dummy.

If Dalia is being totally honest about it, she may have had the tiniest crush on her almost-Uncle Raul. Not, like, in a creepy way, but there are some things you know in your life, even when you're twelve, and the thing Dalia knows is that she was a little bit in love with Raul. Before her aunt went and killed him, that is.

She hasn't told a soul about this. Except for Cass. Cass is good at keeping secrets, she says, because she has so many of her own.

"Like what?" asks Dalia. "Tell me one."

"Like your hermit crab is dead," says Cass. "Like I drowned him in the fountain downstairs."

Dalia laughs, good one. But Cass is sincere. "Look if you don't believe me."

Dalia doesn't want to, but she forces herself out of the closet. She lifts the mesh top of the tank on the dresser. It's busted on one side, as if someone was in a hurry to yank it open. She holds her breath against the stink coming out of it as she checks under the tiki hut. Sure enough, no crab.

"I didn't mean to," says Cass brightly when Dalia returns to the closet floor. "I meant to give it a bath, but the fucker bit me, so I let him drown in there."

Dalia nods. The fucker.

She doesn't feel guilty about the crab dying because she hated it. She supposes you can only feel guilty about the things you truly love.

In the darkness, Dalia tells Cass the story about the time that Raul read her palm and she realized at once that she was in love with him. He had just gone and grabbed her hand out of the clear blue, in front of everyone. Grabbed it and laid it flat on top of his very own. It was Christmas Eve, two years ago. Dinner was over and the house was stinking pleasantly of fish.

Here is my present for you, Raul had said to her as he suddenly grabbed her palm like that. In Raul's wide brown hand, Dalia's own looked so tiny and pale. The pearl in the center of an oyster.

Raul made a series of theatrical faces for Dalia's benefit, but they made her Aunt Charlotte laugh instead. "Isn't he ridiculous?"

Charlotte asked no one in particular. She was still wearing the apron she had worn to cook for them that night, with its stains of various bloods and sauces. When Aunt Charlotte used to prepare a meal at their house, her mother complained that it would take her weeks to get her kitchen back in order. Charlotte was a hurricane, her mother said. A stormfront. A force of nature.

While Raul stared into her hand on Christmas Eve, Dalia had a thrilling opportunity to study his face close up. His fuzzy eyebrows especially, which intrigued her for the way they moved like exotic caterpillars bucking around his face. "Dalia," he said, urgently, seriously, pronouncing her name in that special way of his that no one, no one else ever did, "you will have some big surprises in your future. I am sure of it." When he spoke, Dalia saw how the caterpillars wriggled and danced close up.

Dalia tells Cass that sometimes she believes that Raul was trying to tell her something that day. To let her know that he would be dead soon. That she would never be a flower girl. Never get to Colombia to visit his family, to meet his little cousins who were the same age as her, somewhere on the bottom half of the world. Other times, she feels so silly, so stupid for remembering a small moment like this, that lame tears sprout up in her eyes. The nerve of her body sometimes!

When Cass tires of Dalia talking about herself, she insists they leave the closet and go downstairs to watch a movie. Cass claims to have seen every movie in the world, practically. She considers herself an expert in something called "film noir," which Dalia is unfamiliar with, but too shy to admit. When Cass sleeps over, she always picks to watch some black-and-white film that Dalia finds almost painfully uninteresting.

They wouldn't be so uninteresting if she were able to follow what's going on. But the plots of the movies all seem so overly complicated, so hard to follow, that Dalia finds herself instead concentrating on the unimportant details, the way the people dress on screen, or the way they talk sometimes. Why did everyone from the past seem to have some sort of accent that Dalia just couldn't place? The serious, quick words never seemed to be in regular, plain English.

"Do you know what's happening?" Dalia gets up the nerve to ask Cass one night, while her father bangs dishes murderously in the sink, while her mother and aunt shriek, or laugh, from the back porch, where they hang out burning incense or something else equally smelly.

Cass shushes her without answering, and Dalia feels instantly mortified by her own stupidity.

Dalia waits out the film by concentrating on the astonishing fact that because it is so old, all the actors in it must be dead by now. It's a thought that starts as a terror, then a curiosity. And later, something of a comfort.

Dalia and Cass must have fallen asleep in front of the TV. The movie they were watching has been replaced by a new one, a different one. Onscreen, a man who looks remarkably like a former president of the United States carries a chimpanzee in his arms. The chimp wears striped pajamas, or perhaps a prison uniform.

Someone has turned the sound off. It takes Dalia a minute to register a voice calling her name.

"Dally, Dally! Hey, look," Aunt Dead Meat says, the whites of her eyes a curious red. It is a detail that Dalia doubts she would manage to dream up, so she guesses she's awake now.

"Guess who I found in my bed?"

Dalia blinks, waits for her aunt to tell her something terrible.

But to her surprise, her aunt has nothing terrible to say. Instead, she silently holds out the fingers of her good hand, from which a wriggling, indignant, very much alive hermit crab dangles. The paint on the creature's shell has faded to pastel, the word "NASCAR" almost completely worn away. Dalia feels the muscles in her lungs suddenly release in a sigh. What her science textbooks describe in their biology unit as "an involuntary response." The crab was still alive. She thought it wasn't, but then it was.

There was a teacher at Dalia's school who lost a daughter to a terrible disease. He didn't work there much longer after she died. He tried to, but it didn't work out. One day during class just before he was dismissed, a kind, shy girl, the sort of girl Dalia hoped to one day be like, approached the teacher and told him in a whispery voice that she was sorry that his daughter had passed.

The teacher didn't even look up from his desk. He picked up a pencil and thrust it into the electronic sharpener. The class watched as the two of them, the girl and the teacher, just stood there, rather stupidly, watching the machine suck the pencil in with a terrible racket. The teacher held the pencil, and didn't let it slip out, even when it was obviously sharp. Even when it began to grow smaller and smaller and the noise became almost unbearable. When the pencil was almost all eaten up, the teacher let go of the stub and the machine finally shut off. Only then did the teacher look up to the girl. "When you talk about it," he commanded, "say 'died,' not 'passed.'"

From that moment on, Dalia decided always to say "dead" or "died," as in "The hermit crab was not *dead*." As in, it, too, had not *died*. As in, Dalia was surprised by her relief to have learned this.

Gingerly, so as not to wake Cass, who is sprawled insouciantly at Dalia's feet, Aunt Charlotte nudges Dalia over and sits herself on the blanket Dalia has spread in front of the TV. It's the closest Dalia has let herself get to her aunt since her aunt has moved in with them. Dalia's heart thumps. Fear, or excitement. The involuntary response of a body makes no distinction, her teacher says. With the TV light shining on it, and from such close proximity, the scars on her dead arm look almost as if they were glowing, as if Charlotte brushed them against her, Dalia would burn.

"Watch this," Aunt Charlotte says and to Dalia's horror, Charlotte drops the little crab right onto her bare arm, allowing it to scuttle up and over, with its little knife claws, the tender, gouged skin there.

"It's okay," says Charlotte. "I can't feel it. I can't feel any of it!"

She laughs as she says this, as though the hermit crab is somehow tickling her with its terrible claws. As if there was something still down there that wasn't yet dead.

Ryan Habermeyer

LA PETITE MORT

Every morning, the elephant masturbator lures the elephant into the cage by humming Bach. The elephant, blind and tuskless, lumbers slowly onto the hay, kneeling like a prince, obviously in love with the low, languid melody.

* * *

The elephant masturbator continues humming as she administers the sedative, stares into the elephant's wet, glossy eyes as it slips into wherever it is elephants go when they dream. She rubs his trunk. She counts: three, two, one.

* * *

As the elephant masturbator gently arouses the elephant she traces the wrinkles on its skin. Here is a scar from fleeing the poachers. Here a reddish patch that may or may not be an infection. Here are the freckles she's named Larry, Curly, Moe.

Ryan Habermeyer is the author of *The Science of Lost Futures* (BOA Editions, 2018). His stories and essays have appeared in *The Massachusetts Review, Copper Nickel, The Cincinnati Review, Puerto del Sol,* and *Fugue.*

* * *

By the time the elephant awakens the elephant masturbator has scavenged a meal of twigs, roots, leaves, and the last two yellow flower petals in this part of the world. Watching the elephant eat, the elephant masturbator tells the elephant about Hanno, the elephant of the Pope. And Surus, who crossed the Alps with Hannibal. And a nameless pachyderm, knighted by Henry III, who died drinking too much red wine while consoling the king.

* * *

Once home, the elephant masturbator pours herself a glass of sour wine and sits on her balcony, staring at the haze of neon lights and listening to sirens echo, wondering why she stays in this desert, in this city like the edge of a map torn off that nobody bothered to tape back together. She listens to Bach. She prefers the fugues in D minor. She drinks more wine.

* * *

At dawn, the elephant masturbator arouses the elephant after which they go for a walk.

* * *

In the evening, the elephant masturbator arouses the elephant after which they go for a walk.

* * *

At the restaurant, the elephant masturbator eats mealworms sautéed in a kind of yellow pesto with a side of fried crickets. The man sitting across from her talks about trying to save the last butterflies from extinction. He rubs his thumb on the white tablecloth until it leaves a greasy stain. It's important work we're doing, he says. You have a cricket leg in your teeth, she says.

* * *

After her date, the elephant masturbator visits the elephant and pushes fruit rinds buzzing with flies through the cage bars. She rubs his trunk and tells him about the man with the comb over. The elephant leans against the cage, sighs, like he wants to be touched.

* * *

Mwisho, she calls him, which in Swahili means *the end*.

The elephant masturbator sponges water over Mwisho's ears, legs, stomach. She's careful around his eyes. She knows how this will end. Alone, floating towards her petite mort, she imagines the shriveled elephant carcass carried away by devoted ants until there's just a keyboard of bones in the dust. It'd be nice, she thinks, if she was also a sacrament.

* * *

Most of the time when the elephant climaxes there's just a noise. *Poof.* Like air let out of a tire. On a good day, the elephant masturbator collects the sperm in a plastic container. It looks cloudy, like a root beer float.

* * *

The elephant masturbator bottles and seals the container. Scribbles descriptions on the label. Sometimes includes a note. *We're still here.* Ships them at the post office to the scientists she's not sure even exist. She sits on her porch steps and waits for mail that never comes.

* * *

The elephant masturbator closes her eyes on the bed and thinks of Mwisho from the inside out. Organs to skeleton to skin. She feels oddly happy at the inexplicableness of it all.

* * *

Leaving the restaurant, the comb over man takes her hand as they walk through what was once the Great Salt Lake, dried up like a bowl licked clean by a greedy toddler. Kids with red scaly patches around their eyes scare away gulls from the debris. The simmering, arsenic haze steams yellow. The elephant masturbator's eyes sting, her nostrils burn. She wonders what people used to do for foreplay.

* * *

The elephant masturbator powders Mwisho with dust. She shoos away flies. Steals pillows from the abandoned hotels and spreads them on the cage floor. Removes lice. Pedicures debris between his toes. Brushes teeth. When the teeth gleam ghoulish it's time to start over and powder him with dust.

* * *

The elephant masturbator keeps coins in her pocket. As they walk the coins make a metallic swish. The elephant likes to filch the coins with his trunk. Sometimes the elephant masturbator will do a magic trick her mother taught her and make a coin disappear then reappear behind the elephant's floppy ear. The elephant smiles but does not laugh.

* * *

The elephant masturbator sponges the elephant and rubs away dead skin, counting the moles on the elephant's flank. Larry, Curly, Moe. She's been trying to get the elephant to laugh. The chimps are gone. Foxes, dolphins, cows – all gone. All the laughing things extinct. Even the butterflies, which never laughed, are almost gone, says the comb over man at the restaurant trying to save them. She pulls faces for the elephant, falls off the stool, tries to get him to mimic her: *nyuk nyuk nyuk*.

* * *

The elephant masturbator saves a butterfly caught in a spider's web on the windowsill. Its wing is broken. She squishes it between her fingers, its juices stickying her skin for days.

* * *

They walk and walk and walk. Out of nowhere the desert opens into a canyon. The elephant masturbator leans over the edge. Who knows how long it had been there, this earthy mouth swallowing up secrets and sighs, the scar of some geological castration.

* * *

The elephant masturbator doesn't tell Mwisho her name. She doesn't tell Mwisho about her scars. She doesn't tell him about the things that make her laugh. She doesn't tell him how in the old war the Germans dropped elephants out of planes when they ran out of bombs. She doesn't tell Mwisho how after her father died in Afghanistan she started sleeping on the stairs, anxious to twist herself into something else, disappointed that she is still flesh and bone.

* * *

Mwisho scuffs his foot in the dirt. The elephant masturbator stomps her foot in response, knowing Mwisho will not call her *unlucky* or *needy* or *unlovable*.

* * *

There are so many kinds of laughter, the elephant masturbator tells Mwisho as she traces a finger over Larry, Curly, and Moe. Funny laugh. Mean laugh. Sad laugh. Nervous laugh. Sick laugh. Laughing to keep from crying. Laughing to forget. Dying laughter. Laughing to remember. Which kind of laughter do you want to be?

* * *

The elephant masturbator's hands do not shake as she steadies the syringe and empties the sedative into the elephant. But they always tremble when she reaches for the glass of wine at the restaurant. It's just nerves, she smiles. I promise not to bite, the man smiles. She stares out the window at the desert. Hidden beneath the dust she imagines the skeletons of creeping things fossilized in radioactive prayer.

* * *

Sometimes the sedative frightens the elephant. It gives him bad dreams. He twitches, groans, cries, shakes the cage until it feels like it might collapse. He must be coaxed into romance. At first, she had to reach her arm up his rectum, elbow deep, and finger a golf ball-sized gland until the long grey shaft emerged. But now she knows Mwisho prefers she rub his foot. Elephants speak through their feet, talking and listening through vibrations. So, she rubs his foot that doubles as a tongue and ear, surprised to discover Mwisho has no interest in sex. He wants a lover. He wants words.

* * *

Still, it's a precarious moment. She's been careless before. One wrong touch and the jumbo organ whips back and forth like an errant fire hose, slapping her right below the eye. Sperm bubbles in the dirt. Fool, she tells herself, her ears still ringing hours later. She waits for the wound to bleed but it never does. At night she looks in the mirror as the skin welts and swells and the bruise goes from purple to yellow to grey. She tries to collect other bruises to show the elephant, to hold her skin up to its blind eyes to say, See?

* * *

You speak of this elephant as a lover, the man smiles. Her insides knot hearing love spoken of with such quiet malice. Love is a strong word, she says, playing with her fork. The moon doesn't exist for the tide, the man tells her. What tides? she says.

119

* * *

The elephant masturbator yawns. The elephant yawns too.

* * *

We're lucky, the elephant masturbator says, stroking Mwisho. Some survive and some vanish and some never exist at all.

* * *

There's nobody left at the zoo. Nobody who knows she's here all day, masturbating an elephant, last of his kind. You have nice hands, her mother told her when she was a girl. When she saw the graffiti downtown, *laugh of a lifesick elephant* in neon letters, she went to the zoo thinking this was nicest thing to do with her hands. There was no advertisement. No application, no interview. No training, no internship, no exams on the history and scholarship surrounding pachyderm arousal methodologies. But somebody did it before her. For decades, it seems. All the equipment is here. The illustrated notebooks, the vials, the syringes, the lotions, the aprons, the goggles, the electro-ejaculators. But the elephant masturbator uses none of these. Just one skin to another. And Bach. Always Bach.

* * *

The elephant masturbator bathes Mwisho. His favorite is when she lathers him in mud, but it's getting harder and harder to find water these days. The lakes have dried up. Rivers too. Most nights the elephant masturbator can hear the neighbors singing hymns in the chapel. A graveyard of prayers.

* * *

You're very mysterious, the man says, tracing a finger over her wrinkled navel. I'm nobody, the elephant masturbator says, just a girl from Panguitch.

* * *

The elephant masturbator is tired of all this desert. Sand in your hair, your ears, under your nails, little grains stuck between your teeth. It's like for centuries people whacked off God until there was nothing left of him and now everyone is just waiting in his hot mute dust.

* * *

This isn't living, the elephant masturbator thinks. But it's not dying either.

Lately, when the elephant masturbator hums Bach Mwisho pretends to hide. His blind eyes forlorn. As if he knows something is being stolen from him.

* * *

Lately, Mwisho stares into the bucket as if wishing he was no longer blind and could see his reflection. She wonders if blindness is something light or heavy. She wonders if Mwisho is happy or sad to be blind. She wonders if she keeps giving away her happiness will it boomerang back eventually like a slap in the face?

* * *

Mwisho sprays her with his trunk. He smiles but does not laugh.

* * *

They wander the enclosures together, the elephant foraging here and there or playfully swatting her with his trunk. The grass used to be so green, she apologizes.

* * *

The elephant masturbator knows she can give up whenever she wants. Nothing is keeping her here masturbating this elephant day after day after day. She is not waiting for a *thank you*. She is not looking for anything to fill the void of existence now that the curtain is falling on this thing called ecology. She does not believe this will change the course of the universe. She has no babies of her own and wants only to stare into the elephant's wet, blind eyes so together they can be unorphaned.

* * *

Later, there is just a puff of air. The elephant masturbator sighs.

* * *

In the man's apartment, the elephant masturbator listens to the man play the piano. The ivory keys are brightly polished. Do you like Bach? Yes, the elephant masturbator says. Later, as his tongue traces the constellation of moles and scars on her stomach she wonders if he is thinking about cunnilingus on a butterfly and whether he knows she is thinking about masturbating the elephant.

Mwisho is easy, she tells herself. Bach. Bath. Syringe. Bach. Men are simple too, but also not so simple.

* * *

The elephant yawns. The elephant masturbator yawns too.

* * *

The elephant masturbator stands in the desert at dusk. She wants to be moon, but she knows she is water waiting for the tide.

* * *

The man knocks on the elephant masturbator's door. She doesn't answer. She presses against the door and listens. She waits for him to knock again, waits to decode the vibrations of his desire.

* * *

The elephant masturbator grinds her foot in the dust. She stomps. Mwisho stomps his feet in the dust. There was a time when the elephant masturbator believed he was calling out to a lover, but she knows he knows he's the last of his kind. The elephant masturbator knows he's calling out to his mother, the keeper of elephant lore, asking her for the generational wisdom that vanished with the poacher's bullet. The elephant masturbator feels the ground tremble. The tickling crawls down her spine until it feels like a little death. The vibrations neither bitter nor melancholic. Strangely joyful. Part of her wants to believe he's trying to teach her his language. Beyond the snorts, grunts, roars, and cries. Beyond those low, dull rumbles the human ear cannot hear. The grinding, scuffing vibrations of the elephant foot. The foot that doubles as tongue and ear.

Pamela Painter

JUST THIS

Big Betty who lived one farm over from ours came by to tell my mom and me that Mr. Antonio was looking for a counter girl for the summer. Big Betty worked in town at Antonio's Trattoria and she was still wearing her pink apron, though I knew she'd soon change into overalls and boots to feed her three remaining hogs. Our Pennsylvania farms weren't farms anymore – just the remnants of tilting grain towers, empty door-less barns, and split rail fences sagging like hammocks. It was 1957 and the men who had come home from the war had gone off to the steel mills and factories that paid better than raising chickens, milking cows, or slaughtering hogs. I was 14, and my best friend, Rhonda, was 15. The previous week she'd started plucking dead headless chickens at a factory along with Grace and Lorna. I knew I'd be lucky to get the job as a counter girl. My dad had died three years ago, suddenly, a heart attack right on the factory floor. Since then, Mom's brother off in Ohio had been doing a bit of looking out for us. Big Betty too – like family, like an aunt. "You

Pamela Painter's most recent book is *Fabrications: New and Selected Stories* (Johns Hopkins Press, 2020). Her stories have appeared in *Michigan Quarterly Review, Five Points*, and *Image*, and have been produced by Word Theatre in Los Angeles, New York City, and London.

won't believe the food. Italian," she told us. "Hmph. Italians," my mother said, as if disapproving, but she thanked Betty for thinking of me. Mom worked in town, doing the books for the pharmacy, so she could set her own hours and give me rides if need be. That summer at Antonio's Trattoria would be the beginning of my education about my body, about men, about what I was willing to do for love.

The next day was Big Betty's day off, and she stopped by for me late in the morning, honking her horn in our driveway, applying lipstick in the rearview mirror. "Gotta look nice for the boys," she said. Her polka dot dress hid her weight pretty well. I knew from her drinking coffee in our kitchen that she called Mr. Antonio and his brother Sal "the boys." "And oh, can those boys cook." Years ago, she'd worked at the Trattoria when it was Frankie's Diner and stayed on after Frankie died, declaring that Mr. Antonio had improved the food two hundred percent. "No more tuna-noodle casseroles or chicken pot pies," she said. My family had only eaten in Frankie's twice, waited on by Big Betty, but never in the Trattoria. The lean, sassy high school boys who hung out in front of the fire hall, smoking and whistling at certain girls, called it the "Dago's Diner." They were the same boys who got detention in school, but ended up as Prom King senior year.

Betty parked behind the restaurant, next to the dumpster the Trattoria shared with Meanie's Plumbing Supplies. Looking me over, she said, "I usually go in through the kitchen to punch the time clock, but today we'll go in through the front door." I'd worn a white dotted swiss blouse with puffed sleeves and pearl buttons down the front, and a new straight skirt, hoping I looked worthy of being hired.

I was amazed at how Frankie's had been transformed into a Trattoria. The booths were a gleaming fake red leather, and the dining room's walls had been done up with real live green vines twining above large paintings of Italian landscapes, two I recognized from history class as the Colosseum and the Leaning Tower of Pisa. At the back, the counter and round stools from Frankie's were the same, running almost the width of the dining room and ending at a swinging door that led to the kitchen. The most amazing change was the addition to the left of the tables: a huge jukebox the size of our refrigerator, a spectacle of neon blues and reds and gleaming golds.

When Big Betty called, "Hey Tony," a man burst through the door, wrapped in a white apron and the scents of garlic and something I came to know as fennel. His dark hair was slicked back above a splotched red face and a wide smile. Big Betty called him Tony, but he would always be Mr. Antonio to me. She gave me a little push forward, saying, "This here is Annie. You'll see she's a good worker."

He smoothed his apron over his round stomach and bowed low, repeating my name. When Big Betty asked, "Where's Sal?" Mr. Antonio yelled, "Salvatore, come meet *Ah-nie*, our new girl." Sal – right away Salvatore was Sal – also wore a white apron, though his bib dangled down from his open shirt and narrow waist. His eyes widened at what I thought then was my young age. Later I would recall my white blouse with tiny pearl buttons down the front. "*Buongiorno, Ah-nie*," Sal said, also bowing, but very low as if making fun of his gesture. "Is *bene* that Tony already hired you." A pink scar under his right eye seemed to dance when he spoke. We agreed that I would start the next day. Mr. Antonio said, "Betty will show you ropes, she knows this place better than me." She was Betty here, I realized, and I made a mental note to drop "Big." Mr. Antonio produced a bent timecard, wrote my name on it with a flourish, saying it would be waiting for me tomorrow. Sal had gone into the kitchen to retrieve two pink aprons. As he handed them over, he winked, assuring me that he was *molto bene* at tying bows. "Ciao, ciao," Betty said, rolling her eyes and leading me out the door.

"Better than plucking chickens," she said on the way home. When we arrived at my farm, she handed me a hairnet with little sparkles in it "for tomorrow." I was already going through my summer clothes, choosing what I'd wear, maybe buying a new blouse or two. "She passed the test," Big Betty told my mom, who that night would proudly write her brother a letter about my new job.

The next day, Mom dropped me off at the back of Mr. Antonio's in time for Big Betty – Betty – and Marge's weekend evening shift. The Trattoria's tiny kitchen was crammed with stainless steel shelves and gleaming countertops. Crates of vegetables teetered along one wall. One surely held more garlic than could be found in all the kitchens of our town. In greeting, Mr. Antonio waved a wooden spoon from his place in front of a huge iron stove with six burners, flames alight under two big steaming pots. Sal abandoned scrolling out what I soon learned were delicate sheets of pale, yellow pasta, and insisted on helping with my apron – actually a half apron, no top. "Give here, *Ah-nie*," he said and I handed it over. He motioned for me to turn around so my back was to him, and I felt a puff of breath on my neck as he reached to draw the apron around my waist. Behind me, the two sashes slowly tightened into what must have been a perfect bow. "Perfecto," Betty said, appearing through the swinging door. She gave Sal a swat with her order pad saying, "Gotta watch out for Sal," and they all laughed – Mr. Antonio, Betty and especially Sal – as she led me back through the swinging door to the first day of my first job.

My station was behind the counter. There I took care of customers seated on stools, served desserts from a circular case with shimmering glass doors. Within two weeks I was ringing up checks at the cash register. The daily special was written on a chalk board – today's said "spaghetti with olives and tomato sauce," which Sal told me was really *spaghetti alla puttanesca* – still my favorite pasta. Betty had pointed out the wine kept in its own refrigerator in the kitchen, poured by Sal and served by her or Marge in glass carafes. "We're very fancy here," Betty said, laughing at my surprise. Frankie had served coffee, tea and sodas. Our menu offered "Wine: White or Red."

That night wasn't too busy. I learned where things came from and went – glasses, plates, desserts. How to swoop down a red paper placemat in front of a customer, and offer a menu with a sprightly "good evening." Our customers were people from town out for a night of not-cooking. The Gosses who owned Woolworth's Five and Dime, two teachers from the county schools, our mailman who sat at my counter, the librarian wearing "Midnight in Paris" perfume. Soon the booths and tables were full, even some of my counter stools. I wrote orders on a little green pad and walked them into the kitchen to Mr. Antonio, who patted each one as if blessing it. Sal moved between the six-burner stove, his glistening salad bar with its array of knives, and the small refrigerator storing the white wine. Not many people ordered wine. Betty stopped by the counter a couple of times to see if I needed anything. On the jukebox Johnny Mathis was crooning "It's Not for Me To Say" or Elvis pleading "Don't be Cruel." Betty grimaced when someone played The Coasters' "Yakety Yak" or Little Richard's "Tutti Frutti." Rhonda kept close track of the top 100 songs, and our jukebox would have made her green with jealousy.

Hours later, as Betty and I punched out, she told Mr. Antonio that my first night had been a success. He gave a thumbs up from where he was wiping down the six-burner stove. "So, that means *Ah-nie* will come back," Sal said. He was sharpening knives at his salad counter and reached over to give my apron's bow a tug, undoing it. I giggled and luckily caught it before it hit the floor. The small pocket was weighed down with nickels and dimes from tips. I felt grown up and rich and pretty.

On the way home, Betty told me how Mr. Antonio and his brother had come to live in our Western Pennsylvania town. She said their parents had been killed in Mussolini's terrible war. He'd deserted the army to care for his brother, who was almost starving. Mr. Antonio had been 23 and Sal 16 when they survived by hiding in the forests above Naples, foraging for food, trapping rabbits, before they became refugees. "Most of the time he don't talk about it," Betty said. "He said Sal don't like him to bring back those days. They came to live with a cousin two towns over in that big Italian community. No money, looking for work and that's how they came to cook for Old Frankie. They learned English fast, and cooked what he told them to. Occasionally Frankie would let them do what he called 'an I-tal-yun night' but mostly it was his recipes. He didn't have any kids, and when he died five years ago he left them the restaurant. They got families now. Kids," Betty said. "Hard workers. But we have our fun. Tony likes to sing. And Sal, he's a joker and a genius with desserts. Wait till you get a taste of his cannoli."

Several weeks later, on a slow, rainy night Mr. Antonio came out of the kitchen, a towel thrown over his shoulder. He turned the *Open* sign on the door to *Closed* and dinged the register to slide out a handful of dimes. "Is time for real music," he told me as he crossed the room to stand in front of the gaudy jukebox. I was marrying the ketchup bottles like Betty taught me. She said it sounds sexy but it's just a matter of carefully balancing one upended ketchup bottle on top of another, both standing straight up. Married. Rhonda howled when I told her about marrying the ketchup bottles at the end of shift. She said, "You don't want to know about dead chickens."

Mr. Antonio was slapping through the jukebox's metal pages, punching buttons, and suddenly, a different sort of music filled the trattoria. I abandoned my eight ketchup bottles and listened in surprise to the music coming out of our jukebox. It was a woman's voice unlike any I'd ever heard before.

Mr. Antonio noticed me just standing there and gave a little wave with his towel.

Feeling caught out, I immediately went back to work, uncoupling my ketchup bottles, wiping their red necks, screwing on their tops.

"No, no, *Ah-nie*," he said frowning, and waving his towel again. "No more – *ferma* – with the ketchup sauce. Just listen." I heard soaring notes rising to a great height and falling, falling. Round trembling notes. Notes rippling here and there. Behind the woman's voice was the largesse of what I later learned was a full orchestra, housed in an orchestra pit below stage, and led by the precise baton movements of a conductor in tails.

When it ended, Mr. Antonio said "It is 'Sempre libera' by Giuseppe Verdi. Will play again for you. Listen," and he put more dimes in the jukebox and after checking to see that I was listening, he stood there with his eyes closed, his hands folded on his aproned paunch. Twice, from the kitchen Sal's voice joined that of the singer, and each

127

time Mr. Antonio called out "Sal, Sal. *Silenzio.*" At the end of the song, he said to me, dabbing at his eyes with his towel, that those songs were called *arias,* and they were telling the most important parts of the story. "Violetta is in love, but torn between two men. She must choose. Oh that Verdi, he can break your heart."

I was alone the next day before I started work so I clinked through the jukebox's metal pages looking for last night's magic. I went past "Maybelline" and all the Johnny Mathis and The Shirelles, and came to Giuseppe Verdi's "Sempre Libera" in something called *La Traviata.* Almost disbelieving, I put a dime into the slot and pushed Y-4, then I backed up to one of my counter stools to sit and take it in. What was it? What did I feel? I only had my life so far – Rhonda, school, giggling at boys pushing each other in the halls to show off, home, a one-time farm in thrall to weather. But here this music was my weather – a mist, a downpour, a sleet-storm, a hurricane of sound. From that day on, when I was alone and cleaning up, I changed my nickel tips to dimes, and wove past the six tables to where the jukebox stood, waiting. Mr. Antonio would knock on the little window to the kitchen and grin approval of me and my music, sometimes slipping more dimes into my tips cup. Sal would often sing along, or do a drum roll with wooden spoons, or clang pot lids together like cymbals with Mr. Antonio shushing him. And so began my education.

The first time I played "Un bel di vedremo," Mr. Antonio emerged from the kitchen, his forehead glistening from the steam of the discarded pasta water. "Do not drown the pasta, cushion it with water," he would say. "You Americans, you drown your pasta." We listened to "Un bel di vedromo" together until the end. "That one, that aria is from *Madame Butterfly,*" he said, his eyes dewy and sad, his mouth downturned. "Ah, poor Butterfly. Her name is Cio-Cio San and Pinkerton is no good to her. It's a long, tragic story. Sometime, I tell you." But it wasn't until years later that I came to know and hear the full story of each opera. I would learn that Cio-Cio San is betrayed by Pinkerton, gives up her child, and kills herself, but by then I was hopelessly in love with opera, betrayed by opera, maybe. But back then, at 14, I wasn't looking for love that I could trust.

In the next weeks, I marveled at the tastes and smells of Mr. Antonio's food. I learned that roasted garlic is far different from raw garlic and a cold-pressed virgin olive oil is more important than butter. His noodles were *pasta,* different shapes, not just thin strands of spaghetti, and had names like *tortellini, penne, fusilli, rigatoni, orzo, farfalle.* Our menu said "ribbons of pasta in red sauce" next to *tagliatelle,* but Sal insisted I learn to say *"tagliatelle."* Chin up, his pink scar glistening, his tongue plying the word, he would demonstrate how the "g" makes no sound. Mr. Antonio would stop and nod his approval as I repeated after Sal "*tagliatelle. Far-fal-le. Tagliatelle.*"

Sometimes on Sundays after Mass, their Italian wives came in trailing kids who went to Catholic school two towns over. Mr. Antonio had four kids and Sal two. They pulled two tables together in the middle of the restaurant and ordered plate after plate of food, all in musical Italian – *pollo alla cacciatore* for a dish that on the menu said "chicken in red sauce," and *braciola* for "rolls of beef in red sauce." You could tell the wives were friends, as they leaned toward each other, their expressive hands accompanying the gossip and stories they were surely telling. They dressed in stern dark suits and white blouses, but their elaborate hairdos were soft and elegant, upswept with combs and sparkling pins. Mr. Antonio and Sal took turns sitting at the head of the table. Each would whip off his apron, pull up a chair, and immediately begin to argue with his distracted wife, or it sounded like arguing at first. To this day, I like to linger in cafes in Bologna or Naples to overhear the musical back and forth of Italian bickering though I suspect it never settles anything.

Toward the end of each *famiglia* Sunday lunch, Sal would show up with barrels of *gelato*, a specialty our customers adored. Betty said *gelato* was the first Italian word that made it onto our menus. Sal would wink at me as he doled out scoops of chocolate and strawberry, feigning amazement that no one wanted plain old vanilla. One time, I was setting up a table nearby when he offered a spoonful to a little girl in a frilly white dress, telling her it matched her dress. She drew back, shaking her head, so he held the spoon out to me saying, "This is *Ah-nie's* favorite." Surprised, I reached for the spoon, but he brought it to my lips, and dutifully I took it in. Then I closed my eyes, pretending to swoon at how delicious it was. "More?" Sal asked, and he dug the spoon in again and handed it to me, full and glowing. The younger kids giggled and the little girl in her frilly white go-to-Mass dress said okay she'd try it. Her mother thanked me with a smiling "*bene, bene.*" Townspeople in the surrounding booths watched and listened in to these family tableaus and mostly smiled. No one ever played the jukebox on the Sundays Mr. Antonio and Sal's families noisily took over the tables at center stage.

I didn't see much of Rhonda, who was hoping we'd need another counter girl so she could leave off plucking dead chickens. Betty said, "if business picks up" to humor me, but the slow afternoons only brought in boys who joked and pouted over Cokes, sometimes with their skinny girlfriends. They played Elvis and Chuck Berry until Betty shooed them out to make way for what she called the dinner crowd. I never spent my hard-earned tips on Elvis or Connie Francis plaintively crying "Who's Sorry Now?" And I never told Rhonda or my mother about the arias on the jukebox, though I don't know why.

In a month I had memorized the numbers of 12 songs – to myself I practiced calling them *"arias."* They were all at the end of the jukebox's alphabet. V-6 was from Puccini's *La Boheme,* W-4 from Verdi's *Otello,* X-7 from Donizetti's *Lucia Di Lammermoor.* Soon I knew every note, every sound of anguish or sorrow or love melting through the words. If it registered at all, customers were probably baffled by my music. One slow evening after I played three arias in a row, Mr. Antonio suggested that when we have customers, I should only play one aria at a time. "Only one is still *molto forte,*" he said, his hand over his heart.

Behind Mr. Antonio's back, Sal winked at me and said, "Our diners cannot be sobbing within their *osso buco.*" He liked to tease his brother, drawing me in with a smirk. I was seated on a stool at his salad station, eating a cannoli he'd put aside for me. At least once a week, he had something for me to try, usually a dessert like this luscious cannoli. "Is Sicilian *specialti,*" he'd said earlier, beaming at my appetite for sweets.

"No. No hearts to be broken here," Mr. Antonio said emphatically. It was also the way he scrubbed his pots.

"But what about our *Ah-nie?* Your arias sometimes make her cry," Sal said.

"You two back to work," Mr. Antonio said. "*Ah-nie* must learn *opera* means work, from Latin. In Latin is plural *opus.*" I swallowed the last bite of cannoli, slid off my stool, and assured Mr. Antonio that I would hold back any future tears.

Sometimes Betty and I had the same shift, and once after I played the soulful "Sempre Libera" she said she liked the change in atmosphere, that she got tired of Elvis and Peggy Lee real fast. Another time, she stopped wiping down a booth to say, "You know, as pretty as that song is, I suspect the woman singing it isn't very happy." This startled me. How did she know? It took several years for me to accept this mystery, how something so beautiful, something I came to love so deeply, was often about anguish and sorrow and despair.

One night in early July when Sal and I were alone and closing up, he came out of the kitchen, and said, "Play 'O Soave fanciulla' from *La Boheme.* That aria, it is the most beautiful love duet." He unwound his apron and tossed it onto the counter, telling me to stop working. Then he patted the stool next to him. "Sit here." Like always, as if to signal the end of that evening's work, he tugged on my apron's sash. "Oh, Sal," I said, laughing, and caught it before it tumbled to the floor. He shushed me, and in a rough low voice he sang along with the music, swaying back and forth, his shoulder touching my shoulder. I later realized I was seeing him anew at that moment: a handsome man, with expressive eyebrows above dark eyes and a sliver of scar, a solid chest, his round shoulder dipping against mine. His eyes were closed as the music swelled, and his voice followed it word for word, and at the end his shoulder remained against my shoulder for seconds past the final note. Eyes still closed, he held his hand on his heart just like Mr. Antonio, but with an intensity I didn't understand.

And then I did. A week later, Mr. Antonio again left early, apologizing for the extra work. He gave me four dimes saying, "Tonight begin with Verdi." When I thanked him he clasped his hands, like the tenor preparing to sing, and then he left with a reminder for Sal to turn the flame under the stockpot to low. I pushed W-4, waiting for the first astonishing notes of "Si un Jour" before I went back to filling salt and pepper shakers. A few minutes into the aria, Sal pushed through the swinging door, crooning *"Ah-nie, Ah-nie."* Then he fiddled with the jukebox and suddenly music flooded the room as if the singers, the orchestra, and the audience had entered this very space. "Come on, Sal," I shouted. "I won't hear my customers' orders." Then we both laughed, because it was now past closing time.

"Stop that," Sal said, pushing aside my tray of salt shakers. Then taking my hand, he led me from behind the counter and through the swinging door into the kitchen. The lights were turned down low and two simmering stock pots on the stove added to the evening's humidity. At his stainless steel salad counter he motioned for me to sit on what I'd come to think of as my dessert stool. But tonight no dessert was waiting.

Tonight he stood in front of me, and said that he had a favor to ask. *Un favore.* Then he leaned against my knees and lowering his gaze he said, *"Ahnie,* just this." Slowly he unbuttoned the first button of my blouse. I don't know why I sat there – my arms hanging straight down, limp, my knees pressed together – but I did. Maybe it was the music. I knew every note and every note to come. I knew when the music would stop. Maybe that is why I wasn't afraid. I don't remember being afraid. I might even have been curious.

I didn't move. I watched six pearl buttons come undone. He looked up at me when he undid the last button. "Yes?" he said. *"Ahnie?"* I could have said no. But this was Sal. The same Sal who pulled the sashes of my apron every night and taught me *tagliatelle* and *far-fal-le.* I could have pushed him away and stood up, saying, "Are you crazy?" But I didn't stop him – maybe because I was still wearing my pink apron.

One at a time, he slipped the two straps of my cotton bra off my shoulders, slid them down my arms. When I still didn't move, he slowly pulled my bra down to where it rested on the waistband of my apron, my apron spread across my lap. Gently, he cupped my breasts in his two hands, saying again, "Just this." His face was inches from mine, and above his scar, his eyes were hooded, downcast. I knew what he was seeing because I'd done the same thing in my bedroom, in front of the mirror, my curved palms filled with breasts I knew were large for my age, my thumbs brushing my nipples. As his thumbs were doing now. Was this so different? My own hands felt full in this moment. I watched his hands. I didn't close my eyes. I don't know why but I stayed there – my arms motionless, my knees pressed together – stayed there till the last note, but I did.

In the sudden silence, he moved first. Breathing deeply, he slid my bra straps up each arm and over each shoulder, then carefully he pulled my bra up to cradle my breasts. He buttoned one button then stepped back, and I knew I was left to do the other buttons. We both watched my shaking fingers. Finally he looked up at me and I remember that we both seemed surprised. "Please," he said, his dark eyes unsure, perplexed. "*Ahnie*, you must not tell."

"I'm fourteen," I said. It seemed unattached to anything.

"I know, *Ah-nie*," he said. "It will never be more." At the time, I didn't wonder what that meant.

I slid off the stool and then like always, Sal suddenly tugged on my apron's sash, and just like always my apron dipped from the weight of my tips. And just like always I caught it before it hit the floor. We both laughed, perhaps relieved to fall back on the end-of-the-night's usual playfulness. Then I punched my timecard, and called a breathless "good night" as Sal bent down to adjust the flame under Mr. Antonio's simmering stock pots to as low as it would go.

My mother was waiting to drive me home. My bedroom mirror was waiting to show me what had happened. I stood in front of it and slipped my bra down to my waist, then I held my breasts. I squeezed my nipples, something Sal had not done. In bed, I hoped for a dream or nightmare to tell me what had happened. Would I tell an astonished Rhonda, who even though she swore to secrecy would certainly tell our friends; my mother who would regret allowing me work at the Trattoria; Betty who might feel responsible for putting me in Sal's way, knowing what a flirt he was I think she would believe me. These scenarios conjured up by my 14-year-old self made a chastised or repentant Sal seem superfluous, almost an afterthought. Most of all, I couldn't bear that it might have been my last evening at Mr. Antonio's Trattoria. The last aria for how long.

Mr. Antonio had ordered more recordings of "our music." He said the jukebox man was coming by any day now for their installation. I said nothing.

The next day, Mr. Antonio admired our closing up. Lights off. Freezer door latched tight. "And the stock is *perfetto*," he said sipping from a spoon, praising Sal's calibration of the flame. Sal greeted me with his usual "*Ciao, Ah-nie*," as if only the music had happened.

The following week, the jukebox man came, rolling his eyes over Mr. Antonio's requests, as if certain I was the Elvis or Little Richard type. The jukebox was shut down, pulled out and restocked. Then once again its lights were turned on as if preparing a stage. Mr. Antonio had requested "Mira, o Norma" from Bellini's *Norma*; "La ci darem la mano" from Mozart's *Don Giovanni*; and Puccini's "Nessun Dorma" from *Turandot*. Soon, I knew them all, note for note.

Sometimes late at night Mr. Antonio gave me extra dimes to see what I would play, always approving of my choice. One night as I was in the kitchen, eating a slice of *tiramisu* and following the last notes of a Puccini aria, he said, "Someday, *Ah-nie*, when you are much older, you must go to the grand opera halls with crystal chandeliers and three or four balconies and a whole orchestra playing below the stage." With sweeping gestures above his stove, the burners off for the night, he described the opulent opera house in Naples where he and Sal visited their one surviving uncle every other year. "Right, *Salvatore*. We must go next summer." Sal nodded, a faraway look in his eyes I knew well. Mr. Antonio went on, saying, "Someday you will know each opera's story – *La Traviata*, *Carmen*, *Don Giovanni*, *Norma*, and *mio dio*, Wagner's *The Ring Cycle*," and here he closed his eyes and shook his head with an angry sadness. "Yes, even the Germans," he said. "Even the Germans."

The next time Sal and I were left to close up I imagined Sal watching Mr. Antonio leave, perhaps trying to resist what he would ask me to do. An hour later, the jukebox on high, he again took my hand and led me through the swinging door to the stool. The lights in the kitchen were low but soon Sal and I could both see that my blouse was open, the buttons undone, my breasts bare to his gaze and mine, bare to his cupped hands, his touch. But this time he stepped forward slightly and tucked two fingers under my chin, tilting my face up to his, bending toward me. Our lips were inches apart. His scar nearer still. "No," I said, my hands against his chest, pushing. I leaned back so far he caught my wrists to keep me from falling.

"No," I said, panting, regaining my balance, my will. I said, "Just this." Freeing myself from his grasp, I looked down at my open blouse, my breasts. "Only this." He nodded, and filled his hands once more till the music ended. And just like that, the night was over. I went home and slowly undressed in front of my mirror. This time, it never occurred to me to tell.

It happened several more times before the summer was over but it was never again more than "just this," though in my heart I knew I could have made it even less. I imagined saying "no" when Sal came to lead me into the kitchen. I imagined Sal saying, "Oh *Ah-nie*, you are make me sad." But I said nothing, told no one. I never said "no." By summer's end, I knew the notes and words of every aria by heart, and though I'd learned the stories of the sad, ill-treated women in *Turondot, La Traviata, Madame Butterfly*, somehow they gave me courage to shape my own story.

That fall my mother's brother said he needed Mom to do the bookkeeping for his growing hardware business, so we sold what was left of the farm and moved to Ohio. I, too, was needed in the family business. So together with Wade, my 13-year-old cousin, I stocked shelves with nuts and bolts and nails, with fans and toasters, and mops and brooms, and learned how to mix paint. A boombox playing the top 100 kept us company and made me miss Rhonda, miss the arias and their beautiful sad stories. I was 15 when I had my first boyfriend, who sang with me in the school's chorus. He was 16. We started at the beginning. It was my first kiss.

Before we left Pennsylvania, Mr. Antonio and Sal had prepared a goodbye dinner for Mom and me and Betty and Rhonda, who was promised my job next summer. She told Mr. Antonio that she'd never eat chicken again in her life. "Ah, but you do not know the *chicken cacciatore*," Sal chided her. He served us two of my favorite desserts, saying he would miss my appetites. I didn't ever say anything to Rhonda about Sal. And I could tell he knew this. It might be my one regret, but everyone has their own story. I even imagined Rhonda laughing and swatting Sal away with her order pad. Or maybe not. The jukebox was never silent, its arias a backdrop to this dinner. My mother was alert to these new sounds, and would come to love opera as much as I did. But I could tell the music puzzled Rhonda, till between courses she perused the metal pages, and was reassured by the Elvis, and Johnny Mathis, and Connie Francis records that occupied the alphabet all the way to the letter V. At the end of the evening, Mr. Antonio gave me a gleaming red record player and my first complete opera, three LPs of Renata Tibaldi in *La Boheme*. Tonight, thirty years later, *Un Ballo in Maschera* is playing. *La Boheme* will be later in the spring. My husband and I sit in the first row of the first balcony at the Met, a seat we've held for many seasons. The orchestra tunes up, a glorious cacophony of sound, violins, cellos, a penetrating bassoon. Programs stop fluttering and fall to silk or serge or linen laps. House lights dim. My husband of twenty years knows my secret and reaches for my hand. I close my eyes and I am listening again with Mr. Antonio, and yes, also with Sal. I'm a young girl with her pocket full of dimes – a young girl marrying ketchup bottles, carrying orders to Mr. Antonio and to Sal in the kitchen, a young girl sitting on the stool for just this, for love.

ESSAYS

May-lee Chai

HUNGRY GHOST

I am writing this in April, the month of the lunar calendar where 清明 falls, the festival for sweeping our ancestors' tombs, for lighting joss sticks and leaving offerings of food so our deceased will not become hungry ghosts, the spirits that roam the earth insatiable, their giant bellies always empty. It is my haunted month, the month of my mother's birth, and of her death. It is a month for personal beginnings and endings. The month when my memories of my mother's hunger, her pain, all that I tried and could not do to fill the hole gaping open inside her, spill out, are uncontainable, a wail.

Once when I was in elementary school, I overheard the mother of my best friend complaining about me. She told my mother that she was very sad when our family moved to town and I started the same school as her daughter. Her older daughter had been denied a

May-lee Chai's essays have appeared in the *New England Review, Longreads, Paris Review Online, Kenyon Review Online*, and the *Los Angeles Times*. She is the author of eleven books of fiction, nonfiction, and translation, including her original translation from Chinese to English of the 1934 *Autobiography of Ba Jin* (University Press, 2008). She has two collections of short stories from Blair: *Tomorrow in Shanghai & Other Stories* (2022) and *Useful Phrases for Immigrants* (2018), winner of the 2019 American Book Award.

scholarship to college and instead an *Asian* girl had gotten one. My best friend's mother was certain this would happen to her second daughter now that I was here.

I remember the silence in that moment while I stood in the hallway outside the kitchen, neither woman knowing I was there.

I waited for my mother to defend me. I wanted her to say, "My daughter is not causing anyone any problems!" Something to absolve me. Or even to proclaim, "May-lee works very hard!"

My mother said nothing.

Shame lodged in my eye like a shard of glass.

I was learning to read the world around me for my place in it as a young girl of color. Every anecdote, every slight, every silence was teaching me that I was not, nor would I ever be, the hero of my mother's narrative.

My mother and I were not the same race. My mother was White, my father Chinese, and I mixed-race Chinese-American. I did not pass for White.

My mother liked to complain when I was a child, and later a teenager, that she had been robbed of a scholarship because in high school "a *Hispanic* girl" had been awarded one instead of her. My mother considered this scholarship hers to win. A teacher had even congratulated her after the winner was announced. "She probably voted for the wrong girl! She got our names confused!" my mother wailed.

Even as a child, I could tell there were holes in this story. Wasn't it a bad sign that my mother's teacher didn't know who she was and could mistake her name for another girl's, and one with a *Hispanic* surname at that?

My mother's parents were highly unstable and moved their family frequently when my mother was growing up. But while my mother was able to tell me stories about her father's violence, her mother's angry enabling, she was never able to blame her parents' erratic choices for her lack of a scholarship or their refusal to pay for her education.

Instead my mother had learned to blame Affirmative Action for her scholarship loss, despite the fact that she graduated high school in 1951, ten years before JFK signed the executive order that would begin Affirmative Action programs in America.

It must have been less painful for my mother to tell this story and blame the Other girl rather than her parents, who kept my mother out of class to clean their home, to watch her younger siblings, to pick up after the fight, the fights, the endless fighting.

Twenty years had passed since my mother hadn't gotten the scholarship from her high school when she first told me this story, but she still complained with a raw fury as though it had just occurred.

I did not yet see how her anger would turn on me.

When I was very little, I remember my mother praying on her glow-in-the-dark rosary. My brother and I climbed into my parents' big bed to wait for my father to come home from work. He often worked late at night, and my mother was afraid, waiting for him to return.

I held the rosary card for her so that we could look up which of the four mysteries to meditate upon after each decade of Hail Marys. Her Catholic education had been interrupted because her parents moved around a lot, in the middle of the semester, three days from the end of school, a week after the start of the school year. Her father was an alcoholic, and they were always looking for a fresh start. My mother had had only one year in a Catholic school.

My mother whispered in the dark, her fingers on the beads.

Inspired with this confidence, I fly to thee, O Virgin of virgins, my Mother. To thee do I come; before thee I stand, sinful and sorrowful. O Mother of the Word Incarnate, despise not my petitions.

My mother was the only Catholic in her family, a long line of staunch Protestants. She'd converted when she was 13 after a nun saved her from schoolyard bullies. As a girl, my mother was impressed that a woman could be:

childless

educated

a teacher

in a position of authority

able to save a girl child from boys

As a child, my mother had been beaten, punched, slapped, starved, stung, kicked, worked, overworked, worked over, assaulted, insulted, harassed, touched against her will, slammed against a wall, struck with a fist, tooth knocked from her jaw.

She forgave her parents seventy times seven times, again and again and again and again and again. She loved them wholeheartedly so that they might return the favor someday. She'd been taught the only way to safety was silence. But lying next to her in the dark, I heard the way her breath caught in her throat.

I remember the list: *The Joyful Mysteries. The Sorrowful Mysteries. The Glorious Mysteries. The Luminous Mysteries.*

They alternated: Joyful Mysteries on Monday and Saturday, Sorrowful Tuesday and Friday, Glorious on Wednesday, and Luminous on Thursday. Sunday we had church so we didn't pray a rosary.

The mysteries were groupings of moments in Jesus's life, but it was too complicated for me as a child to keep track of. Plus I hated CCD and all the stories of suffering and guilt and pain, so I'd just say the words: The Joyful Mysteries or The Glorious Mysteries or whichever one it was supposed to be, and we'd leave it at that.

My brother fell asleep, but I willed myself to stay awake, lying beside my mother, watching as the beads glowed bright white then faded to green then gray then darkness as my mother's voice whispered through the decades, seeking a miracle.

Night after night after night, watching the moon rise and set bluely from the bedroom window, I wanted my mother to see my devotion to her. I wanted my mother to see how much I loved her. If my mother could see my love for her, I thought she'd love me, too.

I wanted my mother to side with me and not with the ghost. But her father had beaten his rules into her skin, punched them into her flesh, knocked patriarchy into her skull, rearranged her teeth to silence her tongue. When my mother opened her eyes, she saw the past, not me. She saw her father, always Daddy, not her daughter, curled like a comma at her side.

It was his love she sought, not mine.

Until the months before her death, my mother insisted that her father loved her, that the violence was accidental. *Daddy didn't mean it*, my mother said. *Mother didn't know*. Or, *Mother provoked him*.

When her father punched her in the face and knocked out her tooth when she was seventeen, when he punched her in the face when she was nine, when he tried to choke her mother to death and she had to run to the neighbor's house through the Indiana night and beg them to call the sheriff, when he told that joke in front of my father and brother and me about being called "Chink" in the Navy and liking it because it was so funny, a White man being called "Chink" because his eyes were so narrow, get it? *Daddy had a sense of humor. Daddy didn't mean it that way.*

When our family moved to a small town when I was twelve, White kids in school called my brother and me names, chink and jap and gook and Chai Manchu and flat face and moon face and no nose and on and on. I wanted the mother who used to take me for ice cream after school. I wanted a mother who took my side. But my mother said, "Just laugh along. Show them you can take a joke." Isn't this what her father had always said?

What does it mean to side with a ghost?

When she took my brother and me to visit her parents when I was eleven, my brother ten, Gramps locked us outside their house while my mother had gone to buy groceries for Grandma. "You brats! You brats are making too much noise!" he shouted, and I shouted back, "We weren't making any noise! We're not supposed to go outside! It's a high smog alert day!" My little brother had asthma, but he kicked us out all the same.

When hours later my mother returned with Grandma and four bags of groceries, I told her what happened, and she said nothing.

When I was growing up, my mother offered a million excuses for her father's violence, as though trying to find one that fit.

He ran away from home at age fourteen, rode the rails with his best friend Charlie, started smoking and drinking. He didn't like his bourgeois parents' snobbery. They wanted him to go to school and become a dentist! "A dentist!" he roared. *A dentist*, my mother echoed. "What's wrong with being a dentist?" I'd ask as a child, my voice below the decibel audible to my mother's ears.

He was forced to play the violin, which he hated. His mother locked him out of the house during the day so that she could clean. She didn't want a *messy boy* in her house.

He enlisted at age seventeen. Although the military wouldn't send him oversees until he was 18 and by then WWI was over. His father, a veteran, enlisted as well so he could watch over his son and the two were sent to France after the war to oversee reconstruction. My grandfather bragged to his daughter this is where he'd learned his gourmet tastes.

Decades later, he felt deeply ashamed when America entered a second world war against Germany. His mother's family was German. He didn't want to be related to The Enemy, this Other, this Foreigner. He was proud of nothing so much as his deep American roots. He taught his oldest daughter to say, "We're Dutch." She was five and had learned to speak German from her beloved grandmother, when the U.S. entered the war. "You speak *Dutch*," he corrected her.

As a young man, in his twenties his addiction to alcohol deepened. He couldn't hold a job. He married a young German-American woman from a good family, and then she fled back to her family with her infant son and her family refused to let him see her. They were as uptight and bourgeois as his mother. He got hammered and smashed out the window of his in-laws' furniture store, but they called the police, and he spent the night in jail.

My grandmother was still a child in elementary school, innocent of the violence swirling in her future husband's life.

It was harder to find work after jail and the divorce.

When he met my grandmother at a Prohibition-era party at his uncle's house, she was seventeen and newly blonde, courtesy of a free bleach job given to her by her older sister to advertise the older sister's beauty parlor. The sister had recently married for the second time, an older man. My grandfather's uncle.

My grandfather was smitten with the blonde teenager. He drank too much. He had to sleep in his uncle's house that night. He rose in the night, made his way to the blonde girl's bedroom, and had his way with her.

(Fifty-six years later, after 50 years of marriage, and four years after his death, my grandmother will say to me, "He raped me" in the quiet of her living room, as I dutifully take notes.)

In the sober aftermath, both families agreed he should marry the girl. *Make a decent woman out of her.* Luckily, my grandmother did not get pregnant; she could at least say, fifty-six years later, *It was not a shotgun wedding.*

My grandmother said they had to wait a year for the marriage before the justice of the peace because she was seventeen, underage, her fiancé 30. She wore a red velvet dress of her mother's, taken in and repurposed for the occasion.

"I didn't know my charms," Grandma said.

After my grandfather is married again, the chances for redemption are endless. He is a White straight married man with one then two, three, four, and finally eight children, he is a veteran. He is and always has been exactly who the Founding Fathers intended to be a citizen of the United States of America. Every right is written with him in mind. Now when something goes wrong, his wife is to blame.

When I interviewed my grandmother about her life when I was seventeen, after my grandfather had died, Grandma said, "When the sheriff's deputies brought him home, they'd say to me, 'You should learn to keep a better eye on your husband, Ma'am.'"

When she spoke to the preacher about the drinking, about the violence, about the fear and the fatigue, the man said, *When you are married, you are like the yolk to the egg.*

"The yolk to the egg?" Grandma repeated. "What does that even mean?"

Later when Gramps found out Grandma had visited a lawyer, she said he told her, "If you leave me, I will hunt you to the ends of the earth and then I will kill you and all the children."

"I believed him," Grandma said.

"Oh, Mother," my mother said, sorrowful and small at Grandma's table. But later, on the drive home, my mother will say, "Mother provoked him."

I remember the bedtime stories my mother used to tell us. The time she said she ran to the neighbors in the night, banging on their door and shouting, "My father is trying to kill my mother. My mother says call the sheriff." And they said, "This is a matter between a man and a wife" and refused. I remember the time she said her father got drunk and cooked the family pets and when she told her younger brother and sisters they didn't have to eat their rabbits, he grabbed her by the arm and punched her in the face hard enough to knock her tooth out. When Grandma drove her to the dentist, the dentist said, "Next time try not to be so clumsy, young lady."

My mother invited my grandparents after we moved to a farm in the Midwest. It was late April, after my mother's birthday, after the thick snows had finally melted, and the mud in the fields mostly dried. The flowers my mother planted were finally beginning to bloom, tulips and daffodils, bright and cheerful.

Gramps was eighty years of age, with emphysema; he carried a small oxygen tank, attached by plastic tubes to his nose.

I was still afraid of him and kept my distance, but he couldn't walk the property, he hadn't the energy. He didn't yell at my brother or at me. More than three years sober, he'd become a genial man, content with the world.

Gramps sat in the kitchen and looked out the window at the brome fields in the back. He dragged his oxygen tank to the front steps and surveyed the cottonwood trees on the neighboring property, the expanse of deep green grass sloping to the gravel road out front, all the dark fields stretching to the horizon as far as the eye could see.

"You've really made it, Carolyn," he said. "I'm proud of you."

It wasn't her college degree (first and only in the family), her publications as a journalist, her art, her teaching, her family (the *chink*, the *brats*!). It was the farm, this American gothic, that finally made Daddy proud.

Three months later he was dead.

And my mother, despondent, began to chase the love of his ghost.

My mother fell into deep mourning. She joined a prayer group whose leaders believed that mixed-race people were a sign of the devil. Their children explained to my brother and me that we were a sign of the coming End Times when Satan would rule on earth for a thousand years. They believed that G-d had put "the races" on separate continents and only the Devil wanted them to mix. Even as a child I could see the flaws in the logic: Why then didn't White people stay in Europe? Why come to North America and take the land that G-d had given to the "red race" by their own reckoning? Because they did not like my brother and me, they did not want us at their meetings. My mother went alone.

The White men who led the group told racist jokes about my brother, me. When their children bullied us at school, my mother said nothing.

When I confronted my mother with some new horror, she said to me sorrowfully, "I don't know why they have to be this way." Then look away. But she never stopped attending their prayer meetings.

I think they reminded her of her father, the ghost who haunted her. He had liked to tell the same kind of jokes, he'd spouted the same kind of theories. Perhaps these jokes, these racist theories made him feel powerful, in a way that his addictions and his waywardness and his lack of control and his deep shame could not.

Perhaps my mother could find no other way to fill the hollowness in her heart, the empty gaping hole deep in her belly, except through these gatherings of White people who had suffered their fathers' rage in silence and sorrow.

My father was asked to resign his job in that small town and had to work in another state. We couldn't sell our house and so he had to commute, back and forth across the country. When he was home, he was tired. He slept or else he yelled at us, bitter at this turn in his life.

White men drove by our house shooting. They killed our dogs, left their bodies in the driveway for my brother and me to find when we came home from school. When my mother called the sheriff's department, they did not come. When my mother had my brother and me post "No Hunting" signs on our property, it did not stop the men from shooting. But we all knew these men were not hunters. Our dogs did not look like pheasants.

Still my mother could not call them "racist."

She spent more time with her prayer group. She left early in the evening to attend their meetings and returned late at night. My brother and I were often alone on the farm.

My mother put my brother and me to work. She decided she wanted a working farm, the kind her father had always wanted. She bought at first several dozen chickens, then three hundred, then more than a thousand. She sold the meat and eggs to her prayer group, at a loss. I was never paid. My days began before the sun rose and ended close to midnight. There was no running water inside the barn that my mother had had built so I had to carry buckets of water from an outdoor pump to the chickens inside. This took hours every day. Every Saturday I spent four hours cleaning out the 360 gallons of liquid shit the chickens generated over the week. In the winter there was no heat, and my skin cracked and bled. In the summer, there was no cooling system, and I coughed among the animals. As the work-load grew, I got less than five hours of sleep a night, sometimes three, then two. When I complained, my mother said, "God in Heaven sees you suffering and he'll reward you when you're dead." I lost weight. My hair began to fall out. I stopped menstruating. "You're so lucky," my mother said. "You don't get sick. When I was a child, I got sick. I nearly died. Mother nearly worked me to death!" I thought, *This is crazy!* But I didn't know to think then when I was growing up: *This is mentally ill.*

My mother put my brother to work in the appliance store that belonged to a member of her prayer group. My brother now delivered and installed refrigerators, stoves, insulation all over town. One day the son of one of my mother's friends tried to kill my brother by pushing a refrigerator off the top of a flight of stairs on top of him. My brother survived by pushing the fridge up two flights of stairs until he reached a landing wide enough for him to get out from under the weight. His back was strained. After that, he was in constant pain.

When my brother told us what happened at dinner that night, my mother looked away into the middle distance, a slight smile on her face, lost in some other memory, some other time.

"He's racist! He calls Jeff 'Fu Man Chai' in school!" I shouted about the boy, trying to break through whatever ghostly spell my mother had fallen under. "He tried to kill Jeff."

"He's just jealous," my mother said, then nothing more, her silence more haunting than words.

Because I worked seven days a week, I had to steal moments to study. I rose at five and sat in the dark with a flashlight to look at my notebooks, afraid if I turned on a light I might wake my mother and she might find more work for me to do instead. I carried notes in my pockets as I did my chores in the morning and night, pulling out paper to memorize French verb conjugations, geometric formulas, the boring tolls of the dead in Civil War battles, which was what our history teacher tested us on. Although there was a visible double-digit percentage of Indigenous students, we never studied Native history, not the Oceti Sakowin or the Six Nations, none of it. When our governor was accused of having raped his Indigenous fifteen-year-old babysitter back when he'd been head of legal services on the reservation, there were no classroom discussions.

I hated school. I found it boring at best, oppressively stupid-making at worst, but I kept up my grades. I wanted out of this town, of this community, this life. I did not know another path for escape. I hoped college might be it.

When I was seventeen, and ready to apply to college, filling out forms, looking at brochures, my mother cried when I asked for money for the application fee one day. "I'm so sorry, May-lee," she wept. "There's no money for your college."

I was shocked. Years earlier, my mother had forged my signature and withdrawn all the money I'd saved for college. When she admitted what she'd done, I'd cried and cried, and she said, annoyed, "Oh, don't worry, it's just temporary. I'll pay you back when it's time for you to go." She *promised*.

Now I looked at my mother. I couldn't even feel anger. Just terror. A coldness descending over my body as I saw my only escape route blocked.

As she cried, turning into a child, I knew my mother wanted me to console her.

"Don't worry about it," I said. "I'll pay for my own college." And I went to my room and sat on the floor, my back to the door, trying to quiet the pounding in my heart.

I studied the college brochures I kept in a box under my bed. I discovered I could apply to more than one school with one application fee if my parents would sign a statement showing their financial distress before a notary public. My father refused, out of shame. My mother did not try to persuade him. Eventually I applied to exactly one school, one with need-blind admission and good financial aid, a day's driving distance so I wouldn't need a plane ticket. I carried the application hidden under my sweatshirt when I went to school. I mailed the envelope myself in town. I did not trust my mother to mail it. I did not trust that if I put it in the mailbox, that she would leave it there unmolested.

I got in with a scholarship.

My mother said, "We can't send out any graduation announcements. Your brother will feel bad."

"Jeff doesn't care," I said. "He knows I'm graduating."

But it was not my brother who felt bad.

After I fled my mother's farm at eighteen for college, I refused to return. Without my labor, she could no longer supply her prayer group with fresh meat. The work was too much just for one person, my brother, to do it all. She told my father and brother, "May-lee has abandoned the family."

When it was my brother's turn to graduate, he did not apply to go away to college. He stayed at home, to help my mother, to work on her farm for free, and attended the local school.

"You are my heaven's blessing," my mother said to him, his name in Chinese.

My mother died at sixty-one when I was twenty-eight. I nursed her through twenty months of chemotherapy but the cancer metastasized to her liver and then she died.

During this time, I cared for her in my apartment while I attended graduate school. My brother and father would drive down from the neighboring state where they now lived and would visit my mother. They took her around town on the week when she felt well enough to go out each month. I stayed in the apartment to try to catch up on my work, clean, do laundry, rest.

We all wanted her to see our love, to side with us, to acknowledge us as worthy of love. We had all been damaged by the years on the farm and the violence of that community. Now that my parents had finally moved away from the farm, now that my father had a secure academic job in another state, we wanted to be victorious as a family, to show the world we were stronger than the racists.

After my father and brother left, she complained non-stop about my choice to study Chinese language and literature. She complained about the Asian-American student groups that I belonged to and the work I did with them and the articles I wrote about our activism. She complained, too, about her mother, all the work Grandma had made her do, and without any thanks.

I could see my mother's illness, even if I could not name it then.

During her chemo, I remember the first time she woke from a dream and turned to me, seated at her bedside, as I graded papers or completed homework for my master's degree, and she called out, "Why? Why did he do it?"

"Who?"

"Daddy! Why did he hit me?"

"He was a drunk," I said. "He'd hit anybody. He hit Grandma. He hit you when you were closest."

But the next night, the same dream, the same question. *Why? Why? Why?* she wailed. *Sometimes Daddy seemed like he loved me!*

The fifth and final mystery.

The night my mother lay dying, I held her hand in mine in the hospital room. I sat at her side, offering her sponges dipped in water to suck on, as the morphine dripped into her veins to alleviate her pain. I held her hand for six and a half hours, as the hospital chaplain came and left, as we waited for my father to arrive, as my mother grew still, no longer turning her head to seek the watered sponge, as her extremities grew colder, until I felt my entire body shaking with cold, as though I were clinging to ice.

I wanted her to feel my love for her. In movies, the nearly dead always offer some final word of encouragement; they awake from comas and find strength for some final act of love. My mother did not wake. She did not speak.

I held her hand tightly, through the hours, as her breathing slowed.

I did not let go until the final breath rasped from her lungs and then simply stopped.

Only a demon leaves the suffering to die alone.

It's been twenty-five years since my mother died one night in April, and I don't want to be forever trapped like her, chasing the dead for love, calling to the air.

What does it take to chase away these demons? There's always a new scapegoat, always someone in power looking the other way. I think of my mother fingering her rosaries, praying for protection, whispering in the dark, trying to hide her pain.

I used to wish I could improve my *feng shui*, mount a *ba gua* to deflect the *qi*, but after my mother died, I didn't hang cloth over the mirrors, I didn't light joss sticks or bow to the cardinal points. I didn't wear white to her funeral. I didn't burn ghost money or leave bowls of rice and plates of fruit before the grave. It wasn't her tradition.

After I cleaned out my apartment, I found her rosary, dusty, broken, fallen behind her bed. I threw it in the dumpster.

I've got her hunger for love gnawing inside me, my belly bloated, my throat constricted. I feel trapped in the sixth realm of human existence, without a shaman to guide me.

So I am excavating these memories, laying the bones out in the air. In the spirit of 清明, the festival of pure brightness, I am clearing the tomb of my own heart, I am building the bridge to the yellow springs. I am declaring my love to my mother loudly until she can hear me on the other side, until I have filled her empty belly and mine with the sound of my voice.

My mother was broken and could not speak. But I can be strong enough for the both of us.

I've seen what it's like to be haunted unto death, my mother's silenced voice choking in her throat. Instead I vow: I won't laugh along. I'll denounce the hate. I'll get out the vote. I'll march in the sunlight. I'll stand up, speak up, shout until I'm heard.

Let me exorcise this demon need for unrequited love, hers and mine.

In the name of the mother, the daughter, and the hungry ghost.

DC Lambert

ANUFEEK, DA WUV TONIGHT?

When my five kids were young, they adored Disney so much that even now, decades later, the moment I see or hear even a snippet of a vapid movie, a catchy song, up spring entire three-dimensional scenes of their childhood.

I stop to buy a coffee at Wawa during my hour-long commute from work, and the piped-in music asks, "Can you feel the love to-night?" and – although I'd been worrying about how to encourage my younger son to take anti-anxiety medication, how to talk to my youngest daughter about her wedding plans, whether to interfere in the schism between my older son and daughter – the image of my then-three-year-old daughter, now 29, pops up instead, over-laying everything else, like color in a black-and-white movie. She's singing lispily, in baby clothes she'd taken from her 20-month-old sister and somehow managed to squeeze into: "An-u-feek, da wuv tonight?"

Yes, there she is, lying on the parquet floor in our tiny townhouse in Madison, Wisconsin, where we lived then, her three dolls care-

DC Lambert has published short stories in *Columbia, ACM, Cleaver, Stand*, and *Connec-tions*. This is her debut nonfiction publication.

fully laid out next to her for a "nap," and her baby sister – now 28, engaged – is trying to climb up onto the windowsill as she climbs on everything, and her older brother – now 31, in medical school – is coming in caked with mud because he and his friends flooded the sandbox. "Wait! Wait!" I say to him as he heads upstairs, mud and all, but I have to get the baby, who may fall. My then-husband isn't home – he works in his lab over 12 hours a day – but that's a reprieve, for when he returns to the mess of three small babies, he'll go on, when no one else hears, about how I'm useless, a piece of shit, ridiculous, no one would ever want me except him. Then loudly he'll exclaim to the kids, his hands on his hips like a semi-dissatisfied boss surveying his territory: "I sure appreciate your mother. What a cook she is!"

But for now, my daughter sings breathily as I scoop the baby from the windowsill and call my son back downstairs and help him take off his muddy clothes with one hand, holding the baby in the other arm as she tries to wiggle out to get back up the windowsill, all while I'm wearing a hapless-and-harried-but-upbeat persona, like a poor player's mask. And all these patchwork pieces are then grafted back onto my Disney memories, so that gradually, Disney itself is infused with a bittersweet nostalgia and a confused and misplaced sense of my own identity.

I pay for the Wawa coffee now, thinking how I believed that time would last forever: my children would always need me, always be adorable and innocent, I'd always be there for them.

"Sweetie, it's 'can you feel,' not anufeek," I'd said with a tiny smile then, or something like that. I barely remember how I responded, in fact, as it was one of the literally hundreds of similar interactions every single day with my three, then, four, then five small children. Why that memory woven into *The Lion King*, and not another? Some oysters create pearls out of the irritation of sand, and other oysters stay empty or even die. So it is with events in our lives: they are re-membered only haphazardly, called up by music or scent or ego or happenstance, like jigsaw pieces tossed in the air. We imagine we have the whole puzzle, until we look closely, or the numerous gaps are called to our attention, or we glimpse a piece we forgot we lost.

* * *

A few years ago, I stopped in Madison after dropping off my younger daughter, who was then in college in Chicago, and visited several old friends. An unlooked-for and under-discussed boon of staying home with small children and a large circle of fellow stay-at-home mothers is that, as with veterans of battle or survivors of a community trauma, you are close for the rest of your lives and can pick up instantly the moment you see each other even if it's been years.

Over one of her decadent delicious breakfasts, my friend Sabine asked me if she remembered the first time we met.

I shook my head. A blank.

She smiled, then said we'd been outside my old townhouse. She'd been with her three small children, and met me taking a walk, my baby in my backpack, my two-year-old son at my side. "He was stark naked," she added. "Just walking around, stark naked."

"What?" I felt the chair I was sitting on seemingly shifting into sand, and had trouble orienting myself. Had I really allowed him to be naked outside?

"Yes," she said, then added that as we talked, he just squatted and pooped on the grass, and I casually picked it up with a bag, and resumed talking.

"Right in front of us! He just pooped!" Sabine chuckled, sipping her mug with the *New York Times* crossword puzzle image. "And you acted like it was nothing. And I was like, 'Oh, that's interesting.'"

Even when she recalled this memory to me, and even now, as I drive the rest of the way home down 295 at 35 miles per hour because of its interminable construction (they've been "improving" this highway the entire 15 years I've lived here), past one of the inevitable police cars pulling someone over, as I sip my Wawa coffee carefully so it doesn't spill, as I drive – even though you'd think letting my naked two-year-old shit outside would be something I'd remember at least when reminded of it, I still cannot. It's definitely one of the missing puzzle pieces, tossed up and sailing off into some abyss somewhere; and I was so ashamed then, at my friend's house with all its light and light wood floors and windows overlooking white birch woods, that I couldn't speak. At her table, I picked up my own mug, then put it down, then picked up a warm croissant, then put it down, and blinked back tears. My ex was right – this was my first thought – I was ridiculous, beneath contempt.

"And now here we are, almost thirty years later!" She got out of her chair, and hugged me, tightly. I could feel the cords of the muscles in her thin arms.

"I was toilet training him, do you think?" I said, stuck on the image of my child squatting like a dog.

"Probably." She went back to her seat. "Who knows what any of us were doing then. We had no idea what we were doing."

And presumably that's why I cast that particular memory into oblivion – because it didn't conform to how I wanted to see myself then, as a competent young mother. Sabine was right, though at the time it was easy to imagine we were pros, as we had no gauge to frame our competence or lack thereof, and the needs were simple, and the detritus of screw-ups would only flower years or decades later.

* * *

I've made so many mistakes, so many ways I've chosen the wrong path, not even knowing I was choosing, not even knowing, even now, if other paths would've been better, not even being able to see a pattern in the choices, looking back, or forward for that matter, except a kaleidoscopic swirl of good intentions and self-delusions.

* * *

But the blank space of that memory somehow sparks another memory: as I pull into my parking spot at last, and climb up the three flights to my apartment, I remember this same son, then three or four, toilet trained at last, fully clothed thank God, leaping onto the hood of my car and begging me to stay as I'd tried to back away from my parking spot in front of our townhouse.

I'd always remembered this with a sort of put-upon humor – "Oh, kids! Just once you try to go out alone!" – but now, suddenly, it comes to me how disturbing the memory really is.

Why was I realizing this only now, I wonder as I pass the neighbor who always makes something that smells like burnt popcorn and the other neighbor with the nonstop loud television? Why this moment and no other?

I hear my Pomeranian barking, upstairs; she knows my step. I in turn know the timbre of her barks, exactly as I'd known the timbre of my babies' cries; right now, she's just really excited to see me.

"Almost home, Ruby!" I call to her.

Had I been leaving the kids with a babysitter or with my ex-husband then? I think I was going out with my ex? I remember my ex, a concerned expression on his face, prying my son off the hood of the car and setting him down on the sidewalk. But then, if I was going out with my ex, where was the babysitter? I don't remember a babysitter. I just remember my son staring at me through the windshield, with desperate deep terror in his eyes, gripping his tiny hands on the crack of the hood, my ex carrying him back screaming into the house.

No. I left alone. My ex stayed inside. I was alone in that car. Why didn't I follow my son inside? Why didn't I ask, when I got home, why he'd been so upset? Or had I, and I just don't remember? Or was it that I didn't want to see? I was too inexperienced. As a young mother, I was encouraged to treat their fear of abandonment – at bedtime, or an evening out – as an expression of the self-centeredness of small children. "Don't let them manipulate you," was a common piece of dispensed wisdom. My innocent child.

* * *

When I reach my apartment, my dog grunts and twists her tiny body in her ecstasy to see me. "Let's go for a walk!" I say. "Leash? Where's your leash?" She looks at it, then back at me, and I put it on her, and we go outside. At 57, I'm living alone for literally the first time in my life (I married at 19, divorced at 44, my five children then ages 8 to 18). I'm officially "empty nest," a silly term implying my confusion and loss is a neurotic, female response to a natural process even birds understand.

Outside, I stop my dog from running into the street to attack a garbage truck. ("She thinks she's a guard dog!" I shout at the men, and they laugh.) "Good girl," I tell my dog as she confidently trots back upstairs to our apartment. "Let's get something to eat. I'm hungry, are you?" I'm so used to talking my thoughts in order to teach little ones how to speak, so used, too, to being with someone at all hours, that I've transferred all that to my dog. She lifts her liquid eyes to me, hopeful for scraps of food and love.

* * *

As my kids grew, the memory of my small daughter incorrectly singing *The Lion King*'s lyrics became shiny and ossified, as though I'd laminated it, probably because, unlike the pooping incident, or the leaping-on-the-car incident, it illustrated something I wanted to remember about myself or my daughter.

"And then I said, 'It's not 'an-u-feek'; it's 'can you feel the love tonight' and she says" – I'd give a small laugh to whomever I'd be telling this story to (I realize this only now, microwaving some leftover broccoli and ziti) – "'NO! It's ANUFEEEEEEK!'" I'd laugh, encouraging my listener to laugh too. I think this was meant to show her adorable three-year-old stubbornness, but it had an unintentional undercurrent of chaos, things being barely in control. Which was the actual truth.

In my kitchen, I peel some chicken skin from the leftover roast chicken I'd bought at Costco and hold it out to the dog. "Some yummy chicken," I say, as she delicately takes it from my fingers. Then I sit down to eat my dinner, my dog gazing hopefully at me for some more chicken. I'm trying to read a book on Kindle on my phone – which I've propped up on a roll of toilet paper I'd set on the table a while back and somehow haven't managed to move back to the bathroom yet – but find myself reading the same paragraph over and over. I hold a small stalk of broccoli by its stem and twirl it, thinking of the overall pattern of the rings of memory, the giant puzzle of our lives with our illusion the puzzle is whole and makes sense, and I'm pierced by a nostalgia so sharp it hurts.

This child who stubbornly shoved her legs into her baby sister's onesies and sang, believing herself to be a beautiful singer, who called broccoli "trees" and made a game of eating it, pretending she was a giant – this child no longer exists.

The adult she's morphed into bears some similarities – she has a gorgeous operatic voice in point of fact, and uses her stubbornness, ripened into tenacity, to help build her career as an artist – but mostly, that small child, with her particular wants, fears, passions, hopes, is gone. In her own adult perspective, it's still there inside her, like a nesting doll. And in some ways, that's true. But in other ways, the small child is just gone – her high voice, her need for a blanket she called Mimi, her insistence that she had to wear Minnie Mouse clothes and nothing else so that I had to scour garage sales to get her clothes until my friend Naomi came up with a genius idea of buying a Minnie Mouse pin to put on any clothes, so she "always had Minnie with her." (Perhaps predictably, the moment it became easy to wear Minnie by simply pinning her on a shirt, my daughter lost interest in her, and went on to a new obsession, pink ponies.)

And so, yoked onto that memory of her singing from *The Lion King* is an intense sorrow that this child with skin so delicate the blue veins would show through, her long skinny legs like a colt's, carrying her blanket for years until it disintegrated – this child not only doesn't exist anymore, but I didn't know what I had when she did. If youth is wasted on the young, parenting of the young is wasted on young parents.

* * *

I took it for granted, I think, both that they'd always be young, that I'd always have to use the toilet with one of them watching me, that I'd always smile at their sweet childish mistakes with that confidence I was figuring out this motherhood thing; and simultaneously, that they'd grow up and leave and be successful and I'd be free – which, I believed, would happen as suddenly as a door closed.

"Finished at 40!" one of my friends in Madison often said, since she'd had her third child when she was only 22 – so, at 40, they'd all be out of the house, she believed, and she could move on with her life. All of us young mothers believed it would be like that. We

were both immersed in the small and large joys and worries of raising our babies, and looking forward to the time we wouldn't have
to worry about them at all. This would magically happen when they
"turned 18" and became an adult. We would then – it was assumed –
return to the selves we'd been Before Kids, and think only of ourselves, and not worry or fret or be sleepless.

"We'll be able to shit in peace!" my friend Naomi said.

The physicality of early child-rearing was the only type of parenting we knew then, and we thought that was what mothering was –
exhaustion from lack of sleep, constant chasing, picking up messes,
wiping down messes, getting water for them in the middle of the
night, wiping shit from butts and snot off our pants, worrying about
feeding them properly or nursing them through illnesses or getting
them to sleep or shouting over screaming children for conversa-
tions, and desperation for time, any time, alone.

And we were so new at it – while feeling like old hands – that we
still believed it was a sort of aberration. (Even as we simultaneously
believed it was our eternal, endless state. "The minutes drag, but the
years fly by," many people said, but we didn't really believe it: the
minutes dragged too much and the years that would be flying were
so far in the future as to seem unreal and unattainable to us then.)

Simone, an "older mother" – at the time, this meant her kids were
teens – heard Naomi imagine the paradisiacal moment we'd be able
to poop without a toddler staring, and said, "Oh, little kids, little
problems, big kids, big problems."

This was when my kids were something like five, three, and one.
We were at a coffee. I wondered at the time why Simone rarely came
to our coffees, which I found glorious – two or three hours once a
week, all of us mothers gathered together, eating, drinking coffee,
while our kids played. This was the early 1990s, but it may as well
have been the 1960s, or the 1920s for that matter. We were living at
University Houses in Madison because our husbands were all fac-
ulty at the university. We'd open our doors and the kids would run
outside and play. It seemed idyllic then, at least for me, at least as
long as I was wearing my mask. (My ex mother-in-law, who took
pleasure in puncturing my joys much as a small child runs around
puncturing balloons at a party, said to me when I excitedly told her
I'd be hosting the coffee that week: "Oh yes. I remember doing things
like that, when the kids were very small. You grow out of it.")

Simone's comment annoyed me and Naomi. "It's like she has no
memory of what all this is like," Naomi said when it started raining
during the coffee, and we had to rush inside my little townhouse,
gesturing at "all this," dozens of small children and babies running

around and climbing on us and each other. Anna's daughter grabbed a stuffed lion and sang, "Oh I just can't *wait* to be king!" And Naomi's daughter Sophie said, "Let's play mama don't be sessabee!" and several kids ran upstairs to my bedroom.

Simone came over to me. "You shouldn't let them jump on your bed."

I pretended to not hear her and, affecting absent-mindedness, wandered away. I didn't know how to express what I was feeling – she obviously thought, as a more experienced mother, that I was being foolish to let the small kids jump on my bed (I could hear them through the ceiling, the dim thuds, the squeak of the coils, the chant, "Mama don't be sessabee, mama don't be sessabee"), and maybe I was, but on the other hand, it gave them a lot of joy and it was harmless and, most importantly, it gave me five minutes alone. Well, not precisely alone, as I was holding my then-youngest at my hip, but alone enough that I could have a conversation.

I wandered over to the dessert table and grabbed a huge slice of chocolate cake (I was 31 at the time, and breastfeeding, so I could eat practically unlimited amounts of food; now, if I so much as looked at that cake, I'd gain weight. But this too I didn't see at the time, and thought I'd be able to snack on such food forever.)

Naomi, as always, knew what I was thinking. She took some cake and nodded in Simone's direction, "If I ever forget what this shit is like, you can officially punch me."

We both laughed. I couldn't imagine forgetting, but when I saw Naomi recently, visiting Madison again, she'd forgotten it almost entirely, simply remembering all her mistakes and none of our joys. I had to remind her of her delicious homemade oatmeal-cherry cookies she'd make while our kids would watch and re-watch *Donald In Mathemagic Land*, or the remarkable children's outfits she designed and sewed from scratch.

Mainly she tortured herself with her adult daughter Sophie, who'd grown into a brilliant woman who'd gone to Harvard, and had dreams of being on the Supreme Court, which seemed entirely possible – and who, beginning at 21, was diagnosed with schizophrenia, then bipolar, then autism, then two different personality disorders, then back to schizophrenia. Now 33, she'd been fired from several low-level jobs and didn't work at all, and lived on food stamps, disability, and her parents' generosity. But she insisted she was totally fine and refused to go to a psychiatrist anymore. Naomi and her husband had spent over $100,000 on various touted treatments they couldn't afford; they were now in massive debt, plus Naomi's husband had had prostate cancer and had taken an early retirement. Plus, Naomi's mother had dementia, and her brother lived 2,000 miles away, so she was the one who visited her mother every day and took care of her when she'd contracted pneumonia and was convinced the staff was poisoning her. This all sounds almost intolerable, but honestly, nearly every woman my age has intolerable stories like these.

Only we don't talk about it.

It's a weird race we're running, a Red Queen's race in which, instead of running and running and never moving, we talk and talk, and never say anything. Rather than unbosoming our souls as we used to, or, at least, what we regarded as our souls – the deeply important job of raising our children – we now hole our souls in our bosoms, so no one can see, not even us.

I used to feel part of an enormous chain of mothers extending around the world and across time, in poetry, music, art, commercials, movies, books, in the structure of parks and the signs at parking lots. I played a critical role, a topic of fascinated and vitriolic discussions and debates and special considerations and contempt and worship.

Have mothers always been silent and silenced once we've turned into dried-out husks from so much nurturing, our seeds scattered? Think of all the ink spilled, the energy of commerce and industry, all the sound and fury devoted to mothers with young children – then contrast that with mothers of adult children.

Is it any surprise we thought we'd stop mothering once our kids were grown?

Our nests aren't empty; we're still here; sometimes, we peck at the dross, the leftover worms, bits of twigs, poop. And sometimes we have to rescue our birds and return them to the nest. And sometimes we have to toss them out. And sometimes – most commonly – we have to cheep at them from a distance, or fly out to their nests, then return to our own haunted nest, pretending we never flew out at all.

* * *

Naomi was telling me her therapist had told her to do "tough love" with Sophie. "What does that even *mean*?" Naomi said.

I was at her house again, which was decorated with dozens of her father's paintings (he'd been a gifted, failed artist, who'd gotten his MFA from a top art school, never launched his career, and died of a heart attack at 42). "She says I've tried everything and nothing has worked, so what have I got to lose? What have I got to *lose*? Does she even know me? I mean seriously, does she know me? I can't kick my own daughter to the curb. I just can't. Remember Lisa? What have I got to lose!" This was a horrific incident with a mutual friend of ours whose son committed suicide at 22 while she was caring for her husband in the hospital, then whose daughter rapidly deteriorated. After a few years of desperately running from specialist to specialist, hospitalizing her, getting her into programs, not knowing what else to do as the daughter lay on the couch without talking or eating or moving, she and her husband were advised tough love, and listened. The daughter killed herself a few months after they'd set her up in her own apartment.

"How can you tell when tough love is right and when it's dangerous?" I wondered aloud. "Are you supposed to do trial and error with your kid?" And for a moment I was overwhelmed with a cascade of images of Naomi worrying about Sophie, brushing her long white-blond hair with the baby curls at the bottom that her husband loved so much, holding Sophie's party at the fire station because she'd wanted to be a firefighter when she grew up, so many images that blurred together in a kind of gestalt of Naomi with her plump arms reaching out to her daughter, her mouth open in worry, love, joy.

"It's not your fault," I said to Naomi, perhaps speaking to myself as well.

Her pale blue eyes filled with tears, and she picked up one of her beloved dachshunds, massaged its long ears, and said, her voice muffled, "I don't recognize her now. My God. She chopped off her hair. She weighs like 80 pounds. She was always so driven and – and – and – . Did you ever imagine it would be like this?" She looked up at me abruptly, still massaging her dog's ears. "When you held that adorable baby in your arms?"

* * *

When my kids were small, I had a friend in her seventies, a sort of mother figure as my own mother was dying and 1,000 miles away. One day she looked exhausted and I asked her if she was okay. She said she'd gotten almost no sleep the night before. Before I could ask if she was sick, she said, "My 43-year-old is in the middle of a terrible divorce. My 46-year-old is still not married, and badly wants to be. And my 48-year-old is stuck in a terrible job he can't quit."

"Wait," I said, horrified by a sudden realization. "This never ends?"

"Nah." She shrugged. "They're always your babies, you're always their mother."

* * *

There is an undefined age in which children stop becoming our primary responsibility, at least ostensibly. This may seem obvious, and it is from the perspective of the adult child: for them, they simply become adults.

It's not obvious at all from the perspective of the mother.

For so many years, when they were teens, I'd wake up at 5 a.m., teach all day, then come home to make dinner, and basically do my second shift, which didn't end until about midnight. I was often so exhausted, I'd fall asleep on the couch at 9 p.m., my phone at my ear and my ungraded student papers spilling onto the floor, and wake up instantly the moment any of my kids needed me to pick them up – from theatre rehearsals that went until 11 p.m., baseball or football practice, games, lessons, field trips, appointments, friends' houses. I'd spring up like a puppet on a string, dash out of the house with my hair sticking up all over the place, and pick them up or drop them off or pick up a forgotten poster board needed for a project the next day, a forgotten $150 baseball mitt left at school.

Then, all at once, I was expected to simply stop.

But also not stop.

Apparently, I'm expected to know when to speak, when not, what to say when I do speak, when to intervene, when not, when to fly out and scoop up my kid, when to tell them to work through it. But the rules are never defined or even spoken of even as the stakes are stratospherically higher – while they choose the partner they will be with for the rest of their life, or navigate their careers, or deal with health issues (this is the worst), I must stand to the side, essentially wringing my hands or doing my best to not think of it all. Whereas just a mere five years earlier, I was up until 3 a.m. wiping their vomit from the bathroom floor, or anxiously waiting for them to come home after a night of partying, or taking them to a therapist it took 50 hours of intensive research to find and tons of money to pay for.

The clarity and certainty of parenting falls in inverse proportion to their age – the older they get and the more experienced you are, the less certain you are of how to parent and the more is at stake. Till they reach adulthood and you have no idea what the hell to do or say, and very little power over your adult child, even as they're making idiotic decisions that may impact their entire lives. You have to simply watch and take it. Or sometimes speak out. But only in a certain way. Or sometimes lend a helping hand. But partly. Or some-times give them money. But not too much. Unless they need it. Or sometimes open your door to them. If they need it. Maybe. Or at most, timidly ask something like, "Have you thought about – ?" Or something. I'm terrible at that sort of stuff. Who is good at it though? Do you know?

* * *

When my kids were babies, I joked they'd made a secret pact to keep me sleepless at night: I'd get something like an hour of sleep before my baby would need to breastfeed; then, as I sleepily settled back in bed, my two-year-old would scream with night terrors for over an hour, unaware of anything; finally, I'd get her calmed, crawl back to bed – and my eldest son would call out, in his thirsty-in-the-middle-of-the-night phase. He'd indicate this by heavily panting, and wouldn't accept a cup left by his bed. I'd pop back up and hand him the sippy cup, which he'd gulp in one minute, then sigh deeply, and lay back down. I in turn would go back to my room, close my eyes at last – and my baby would cry again to nurse. Like a game of whack-a-mole. In the morning, my ex would express astonishment I was so tired. "But you went to bed at 9:30 last night, and it's" – he checked his watch – "It's 6:30 now." He tilted his head in his best imitation of a puzzled manner. "That's nine hours of sleep. You sure you're okay?" (I tried to tell this story to sketch an illustration of why I divorced – taking on a wry, lighthearted persona – but quickly discovered that even this relatively minor example of his obtuse self-ishness was considered shocking by the wider world. No one likes to hear of suffering unless there's something in it for them, a lesson, schadenfreude, pity, a thrill, gratitude it's not them. None of this applied to my marriage – it was too abusive – so I learned not to say anything at all.)

The point is, even when they "grow up," it's still a game of whack-a-mole, only from a distance, with much less power and much bigger stakes. As I write this, a series of scenes flash through my mind like cartoon stills flashing rapidly to create an illusion of coherence. Which traumatic events should I relate? Which should I obscure? Unlike parenting tales about young children, tales by parents of adults must by necessity respect their autonomy and privacy (so should they for young children, but small children can't tell you to fuck off).

A few years ago, two of my sons suffered major PTSD and depression, each in their own ways. For years it seemed they had a pact too, taking turns with their crises so that there was never a time with no crisis. I'd just flown my son back to his graduate school when my other son phoned me as I was teaching. He'd made a terrible mistake accepting his new job, he said, and he wanted to kill himself, and didn't know who else to call. The kind paraprofessional in my classroom, seeing the expression on my face, said she'd watch the students for me ("This is just a job," she said firmly. "Family is family."), and, under the fluorescent hum of the teacher lounge lights and the electronic hum of the three soda and candy dispensers, I tried to decide whether I should hop in the car and drive down to him. He insisted he didn't want me there. After hours of back-and-forth – with me dipping in and out of class all day, and in the car ride home – he gave a small laugh at himself, and said he was fine, fine, he didn't mean it, he was just being a drama queen, yes, yes, of *course* he'd go to the hospital if he needed, no worries, he just had to deal with the transition, thanks for listening!

I was unable to sleep all night, having no idea (as usual) what the right course of action was: should I ignore him and drive down anyway? But he was an adult. But he'd reached out to me for help. But he said he wanted to deal with it himself and he was an adult. But he said he wanted to kill himself. But he'd laughed about it and said he was fine. But suicidal people often did that, didn't they?

I called his former therapist and the suicide prevention hotline. His wonderful therapist actually called him and spoke to him for a half hour, at no charge. The man at the suicide prevention line sounded unruffled and authoritative, like a banker at a convention. "How about this," he said. "Give him my direct number. Tell him to call me." I gave my son the number but I doubt he called. I was in an agony of uncertainty. But he called a week later, thrilled, to tell me he'd been chosen for some prestigious conference. When I tentatively asked him how he was feeling otherwise, he was puzzled, and I had to remind about the phone call the week before. He laughed outright. Oh, that – it had just been a bad day. (When I told a friend over drinks about this, she said, "Yeah, they shit all over you. Then *they* feel better, and *you're* covered in shit").

Naturally, having a respite meant my other son had to choose this time to call, to tell me he thought he should just quit grad school and come home, and could I maybe pay for his airfare back? Eventually – in an hours-long text exchange, this time in the middle of the night – he worked it through and stayed there.

Meanwhile, my daughter texted me as I was driving into work at 6:30 a.m. to say this weird guy at work was creeping her out and kept "accidentally" touching her and she was thinking of reporting him to her boss. I dictated, tying to keep my text-voice neutral, "Good idea!" Then a thought occurred to me and I asked if he knew where she lived and she texted yes, he'd followed her home one day. So I worried about it all day, wondering if this "weird guy" was violent. Meanwhile, my youngest son called to tell me the PT he was getting at college for his torn ACL wasn't working, and he was worried he'd never walk right again. And as I drove home, my younger daughter texted to tell me she and her fiancé had found a new apartment. I asked her about it, relieved to be genuinely happy for her; for weighing on all my interactions with her was the fact that her fiancé was an alcoholic, but both were pretending he wasn't. I had no idea how to raise this one since she saw the drinking just as much as I did. "Got to go!" she texted. "We're going out for drinks to celebrate!" Then, just as I was going to bed, my other daughter texted, to say she'd decided not to tell her boss, but "just deal with it," and by the way, she'd spotted a mouse behind her oven. I told her to call the landlord, but she said she knew already and to please not tell her what to do as it made her feel helpless. "I'm just calling to vent, that's all. You don't have to race to solve all my problems." The next day she called to ask if I could drive her to her eye doctor appointment as she had no car. Then I called my son to tell him I'd found a physical therapist I thought he'd like (I'd spent many hours researching, asking friends for referrals, etc). "Thanks!" he said. "I gotta go. Are you driving me to the appointments?"

Sometimes being the mother of an adult feels like an abusive relationship in which you simply cannot tell what the other party actually wants because it changes so often and they deny that it does.

I know, I know. I'm a terrible mother for saying that. And of course, they are wonderful human beings, if I don't say so myself. I should just let them figure out all their problems. I shouldn't internalize so much. I shouldn't wear a short skirt. I should be mindful of my biological clock. I should cut my hair short after fifty. I should exercise and take calcium so I don't get osteoporosis.

* * *

How do you parent this adult you're not supposed to be parenting? And how do you let go? When do you let go? What do you let go of? What exactly is mothering anyway?

If the entire goal is facilitating their growth into independent and productive members of society in a way that is true and good for themselves and others – then do we judge our "job" based on how far or near they are to that goal? What are the metrics? How does one gauge happiness or meaning or success? When is this final job assessment? When we've died? When they've lived their own lives? Or do we just spend 30 years of our lives throwing up our hands?

"I don't *want* to know too much," was one friend's approach when her adult son moved back in during a job transition (supposedly). "His big gullumphing body in my kitchen is plenty."

Other friends simply skip directly from "mother" to "grandmother," like putting on an old familiar hat that doesn't quite fit, but will do. Turning into a grandmother, one is then permitted to talk, and post photos of adorable grandchildren. But only gushing joy is allowed. Pity the older mother who doesn't have grandchildren, or who doesn't enjoy being the Betty Crocker of grandmothers, happily dispensing free babysitting at a moment's notice while not being allowed to – heaven forfend – share her decades of experience with her very inexperienced daughter or son (unlike literally any other profession in which mentorship and expertise are admired). Instead we become semi-dotty semi-experienced older mothers who are (what else?) there for them when they need us, but not when they don't.

A friend of mine – a pediatrician, I might add – took time off work to fly up to her adult son's house to watch his two small kids for free while he and his wife went on a vacation. Bathing the baby the first night, she suddenly heard a booming voice over a speaker, informing her it was "past the baby's bedtime." It was her own son, spying on her. The baby, he said sternly, needed to be in his crib. And next time, could she make sure he wore a hat when she took the kids outside?

At the other end are broken adult children one must rescue the grandchildren from. Older women are then expected to give up their own lives they'd just reclaimed. This is also rarely spoken of, except in terms of what good replacement mothers they are.

Would that there were a book, *What To Expect When They're In Their 20s*, *What To Expect When They're In Their 30s*, and so on – but alas.

Eventually, our children return, but as our parents, as with my own mother: I had to bathe her naked and wipe poop off her butt. Our daughters – almost always daughters – become us, with their own circuitous unformed path. That's if we're lucky, of course. Many mothers are simply abandoned.

When my first baby came out, his body slippery and alive, his slate-gray eyes alert to the brave new world around him, I couldn't believe I'd produced something that miraculous out of my own body.

* * *

That screaming desperate terror in his eyes as he clutched the hood of my car.

* * *

When I had five teens and preteens, I took to reassuring younger parents. I felt so secure as a mother, I no longer had to prove myself. "Just do what's right for you and your family," I'd say earnestly.

I didn't imagine a time – only a few years later – when "what is right for me and my family" would be unknowable.

My earliest memory is being in a crib – so I was quite young – and a doll at the foot of the crib started "talking" to me in the most terrifying tone, and I screamed, and I was unsurprised when my parents – I didn't view them as parents; I viewed them as divine fixtures – arrived. They were tall, wavery creatures, indistinct near the top, a bit like El Greco figures, as, with indescribable relief, I reached out toward them.

When my oldest was a toddler, he'd wander slightly ahead of me, but, rather like my Pomeranian, would always know where I was without having to look around.

And they were – are, always are – our most precious creation, so precious we let them grow inside us, and emerge from our most private parts, filled with swollen power.

I don't think I once stopped to think what it was like mothering me, from my mother's perspective, partly because I didn't even view what she did as mothering; I think I viewed it as simply her being herself. She'd transformed, in my mind, from the dancer to the dance itself.

She died at 56, and I've missed her most of my children's lives, but not more than now, when we could have bonded over this bewildering stage I find myself in. Why did I know so much more about coming-of-age tales, heroes' journeys, monomyths – all that structure and order, the lines and arcs, all that redemption and emergence, all those heroes setting out on their path, battling dragons, witches, wizards, monsters, emerging on the other side with a gift or power, stronger or wiser or more magical than ever?

Why did I know this story so well and not the chaotic, unformed, unfulfilling arc of mothering – the story arc without the story or the arc, even in archetype mode, even in fairy tale mode – with no resolution or gift at the end, or even an end, but instead with soundless loss, with sagging womb and flat breasts. The gift is that the gift leaves.

We bleed for our children, our breasts leak milk for them, we weep for them, we lift them high up laughing –

Oh, that I could return, and take them in my arms, and run.

Daniel Mueller

AN INCISION IN THE REEDS

Not long after I turned seven, the world went dark at the edges and my face fell into my bowl of Lucky Charms. I inhaled milk, marshmallow shamrocks lodged in both nostrils, and I might've suffocated if not for my father carrying me to the couch in the living room and phoning an ambulance. All I know for sure is that when I regained consciousness, I was in Fort Hood's Darnall Army Hospital where my father practiced as a medical officer. On a gurney in a bright, white room filled with clanging steel and people barking orders at one another, I looked up at my parents as they looked down at me.

"Don't move," my father said. "If you do, you could wind up paralyzed from the neck down."

I nodded, and my father frowned. "I told you not to move."

My mother explained to me that I had been given a spinal tap. "A spinal what?" I asked.

"Tap," my father said. "The drawing of fluid from your spinal column into a syringe, sometimes called a lumbar puncture."

Daniel Mueller is the author of two collections of short fiction: *How Animals Mate* (Overlook Press, 1999), and *Nights I Dreamed of Hubert Humphrey* (Outpost 19 Books, 2013). His work has appeared in *The Iowa Review, The Missouri Review, The Cincinnati Review, Story Quarterly*, and *Mississippi Review*.

"The doctors had to find out what's wrong with you, honey," my mother said. "It was the only way. The good news? You're going to be okay."

"Of the types of meningitis you could have," my father explained, "it's not the worst. Your body will fight it off on its own, but you'll have to lie still for as long as it takes your lumbar puncture to heal."

"How long will that be?"

"Three or four days."

"Three or four days?"

"To be on the safe side."

"It'll go fast," my mother assured me. "You'll see."

"Look," my father said, "comic books," and fanned a dozen in the air in front of me – *The Green Lantern*, *Captain America*, *Hot Stuff*, *Archie*.

Though he'd likely purchased them in a hurry from the hospital gift shop, I imagined him selecting each with care from the magazine rack at the PX where once, while waiting with my mother in the checkout line, I'd been stupefied by a soldier riffling through one from the X-rated shelf, on the cover of which a nude, four-breasted superhero named Hestia the Beauteous had ensnarled evil industrialists in floods, magma, tornadoes, and avalanches erupting from her four nipples.

"For when it's safe," he said.

In Greeley, Colorado the year before my father was drafted into the Army, a kid I knew from Vacation Bible School fell off the roof of his house and broke his neck. Why he'd been up there at all, I hadn't a clue, but after the hospital released him, ladies from the church, my mother among them, met twice a week at his home to help with his physical therapy, and one June morning I went with her.

When we got there, Joel was laid out on a gurney on the patio, and while one church lady massaged his temples, the others maneuvered his limbs, bending his legs at the hips, knees, and ankles, his arms at the shoulders, elbows, and wrists, trying, my mother had explained to me on the drive there, "to help his brain remember how his body works."

Feet shorter than the elevated bed on which he moaned, I could see little more of him than the appendages that flopped about the waists of the women cradling his calves and forearms, but I remembered him sitting in the churchyard as our pretty teenaged counselor read to us about baby Moses being left by his mother beside the Nile in a basket of pitch and tar and how annoyed I'd been by Joel's deviated septum, overbite, and the barrage of questions with which he drove my beloved Meg to distraction, such that she slapped the picture book shut on the crabgrass and declared, "I don't know about any of you, but killing all the boys makes sense to me."

The next time I went with my mother to Joel's house, I brought my periscope, a toy made of cardboard and shaped like a Z with rectangular mirrors inserted into the joints, which enabled clandestine viewers to look around the corners of buildings without being observed and over the heads of adults blocking scenes of potential interest. As the church ladies worked on Joel, I turned the spotter's wheel until his yawning nostrils appeared in the crosshairs. He raised his head, and the pupils capping his sky-blue irises bore into my one, magnified to thrice its size, floating in a box over my mother's left shoulder.

I hadn't meant to scare him, or maybe I had, but Joel screamed as if he'd seen the eye of God.

In Greeley, we'd lived in a square, red brick house on a corner lot, and in the backyard next to a redwood fence that followed our property line my father had planted corn. The stalks, I knew from the previous summer, would grow until they hid the steeple of the Methodist church we attended. In the same spirit, he'd ordered a yard and a half of manure from the stockyards east of town and spent a Saturday in hip-waders spreading the hovel-sized heap over the lawn, front, back, and sides, with a pitchfork. "Ours will be the greenest grass in Greeley," he exclaimed upon returning from the clinic each evening, assuring us we'd get used to the smell.

My mother indulged him with acquiescent nods, but during the day she cursed him, always under her breath lest I understood more than I let on, for an odor that had only briefly offended the olfactory when the breeze blew from the east now assaulted all five senses without remission, the methane a battering ram to the face and head. You breathed it in and nothing tasted right afterward.

One gray day, I stood inside our screened-in porch with our boxer Duchess when a lady in mourning passed by on the sidewalk. Resentful of the rain that prevented me from playing outdoors, I whispered to Duchess, "Fuck her," pointing at the lady in black who appeared to float beyond the plain of decomposing cow shit, her veil no protection against a stench that spread through the sinuses like a poisonous tide, searing optic nerves and pushing tears from their ducts. "Fuck her, Duchess," I said. "Fuck her."

The dog leapt onto its hind legs, stubby tail wagging, front paws scraping the screens, barks sharp as rifle blasts. My mother materialized behind me. "What did you just say?" she asked.

"Fucker."

In her grip my shirt collar was a noose, my five-year-old body a stiff she yanked into the house. "We don't use that word in our home. We don't use that word anywhere."

From my mother's grumbling I gathered the woman in black had lost her son in the war. From the hall closet she produced a fresh bar of Dial, and in the bathroom, she dropped the wrapper in the wastebasket. She stood me before the sink, where above the tap and hot- and cold-water cranks her neck quivered in the mirror. Below them lay my buzz cut, blond stubble as well kept as a putting green by my father and the electric shears he produced every other Sunday after supper from a shelf in our unfinished basement.

"Where did you hear it?"

"I don't know."

"Where?"

"Don't know."

She turned on the water and held the soap in the stream. "You heard it somewhere. Where?"

I didn't know where I'd heard it, if I'd heard it from her or if I'd ever heard it before. I'd been trying to tell Duchess to sic the lady when the word bubbled up from deep inside me as if it had been there since birth and always would be and no amount of soap would ever remove it.

The hardest part about remaining still was the haunting visions from my past, each an unbidden conviction replete with a death sentence. Yes, I'd taken pleasure in the suffering of a kid I despised. Yes, I'd delighted in the prospect of Duchess attacking a grieving mother. Yes, I'd shot and killed a robin with a slingshot. Yes, I'd gussied myself up in my mother's clothes, makeup, and jewelry and danced around our empty house singing "Getting to Know You" as if I were Anna Leonowens in *The King and I*, as oblivious to my father canting up the walk with his fly-fishing rod and creel as she was of the King of Siam listening to her from his bed chamber.

And yes, just the week before I'd stolen a snapping turtle from its owner's back stoop, having crept on my belly beside the oak panels of his family's Pontiac Safari, which was parked in a carport identical to our own, until the white plastic pail in which the creature was housed loomed but a few feet away, at the bottom of the concrete steps that led to the kitchen. From the moment I'd first seen it, I knew it would be mine – in the same white bucket strapped with bungee cords to the rear carrier of the bicycle the kid who'd found it pedaled up and down our street as if to taunt me. As soon as I had it in my hands, it *was* mine – the cold scutes of its plastron at rest in my fingertips, its carapace sandpaper under my thumbs, the thing itself a football nested in my forearms and shoulders.

The sun barely risen by the time I returned to my house, I yelled to my parents to come outside and see what I'd found by the swamp that buffeted our Fort Hood neighborhood to the west.

"It was just crossing the street," I said. "I'm pretty sure it's a snapper."

I held it aloft, displaying its craggy head, its eyes inkblots caught in amber, its lips pincers. Beyond its hind legs and tail, my father, knuckling a cigarette in the hand that held his coffee, examined it through the smoke and steam.

"That's quite a specimen," he agreed.

My mother, less impressed, made a face and returned to the kitchen where silver dollar pancakes and sausages sizzled on the stovetop. Any joy they'd taken in each other they'd left behind in Colorado, and though they'd spoken to me about the baby that in months would turn us into a family of five, my mother couldn't make it through a day without crying. My father, perhaps sensing an on-slaught of tears, opened the storage compartment at the far end of our carport and unearthed from it an old minnow bucket from the days when he'd fished for crappies in Wisconsin as a boy.

"Now your mother's right," he said loud enough for her to hear. "It's important that you wash your hands after touching it. You don't know where it's been or what diseases it might carry."

The snapping turtle didn't look sick, but that it could be, and that it could make others sick as well, lent gravity to my role of caretaker, and for this I loved it all the more.

"And keep your fingers away from its mouth. You don't want to lose the tip of one."

This stoked the fires of my heart, for I was in possession of a creature with the jaw strength to snap a digit off at the joint, and I imagined the awe it would inspire among kids in the neighborhood, the carrot sticks and celery stalks with which we'd provoke it, the beetles and grasshoppers we'd feed it, the toads and frogs. In it, I saw an emblem of myself: a kid who, for as long as I could remember, needed to retract into his shell, his room, to read, draw, and listen to music, if he was to play well with others. The snapping turtle and I were alike, and it was mine, and as I showed it first to the Spenser twins, Hugh and Merle, with whose family my family shared a driveway, then to Jack and Jim Kraft, brothers who lived across the street from us, I didn't think about the crime I'd committed or the lie

I was perpetuating with each retelling of how it had come into my possession.

"What were you doing down by the swamp?" Hugh wanted to know.

"Looking for snappers," I replied. "What do you think I was doing?"

"But it was early, right?" Merle said. "Before sun-up?"

"At daybreak," I replied, "when living things are on the move, before they go into hiding."

"Can you show us where you found it?" Hugh asked, and I told him sure, that we'd go there on bikes the next morning at sunrise and, if God smiled on us, maybe they'd find one of their own. Not until I'd told the story again to Jack and Jim Kraft, adding to it the armadillo I'd spotted along the way and how the snapping turtle had first appeared in the darkness as a shadow among shadows, inching across the asphalt like a shifting puddle of motor oil, did the fiction supplant the truth, and when the kid from whom I'd taken it set his bike on Jack and Jim Kraft's lawn and sauntered over to us like someone searching for his lost pet, I could look him in the eyes without flinching.

We were feeding it salami with a fork, delighting at the tings! of its beak against the tines, when he said, "Howdy!" and introduced himself as Raymond Calhoun from Florence, South Carolina. New kids were always arriving to take the place of kids who'd left, whose fathers had finished their two-year stints of duty as medical officers and were free to return to wherever they'd come from or set out for somewhere new, the consensus being that anywhere was better than the pit of hell known as Fort Hood. But I liked the place, and one of the things I liked about it most was that all of us were the same. "Gastroenterology," he added.

"I'm Hugh, this is Merle. Boston, Mass. Maxillofacial Surgery."

"Jack and Jim Kraft. Eureka, California. Radiology."

I told him my name, said, "Greeley, Colorado. Obstetrics and Gynecology."

Our introductions made, Raymond glanced at me askance, as if he could see me better through one eye than two. "If I could be any kind of doctor in the world," he said, "I'd be what your dad is," and whistled in the way soldiers had at my mother until her pregnancy was what they noticed about her first and the whistling ceased.

I said, "He delivers babies, big whoop," which was as far as my father had gotten in explaining his profession to me.

"That's half of what he does," Raymond corrected me. "The

Obstetrics part. And a mighty admirable part it is, too. Bringing life – human life! – into the world. But then there's the other part, the Gynecology part. That's the part I believe I was cut out for."

Jim, two years older and a head taller than the rest of us, laughed, and we laughed, too, not wanting to be the butt of the joke we feared was coming, but Raymond spared us by saying, "Handsome snapping turtle you got there," and the Spenser twins recounted the story I'd told them, omitting the poetry with which I'd intended to quell their doubts and paring it down to its unlikely facts.

"So, you got up before sunrise," Raymond said, "with the intention of catching a snapping turtle and, lo and behold, there one was, crossing the street, down by the swamp?"

"You calling one of us a liar?" Jack asked, tougher than the rest of us because of the older brother with whom he had to contend, but when it came to standing up for one another, we first graders were all for one and one for all.

"Nah." Raymond grinned. "We all know the Lord works in mysterious ways. It's just that yesterday I caught a snapper myself – I showed it to you, remember? On my bike?" he said to me. "And today it's gone. Like overnight it either grew wings or built a ladder."

Merle asked if he thought mine was his, if I could've found it after it had gotten loose. "Doubtful," he replied. "But there is one way to find out."

"What's that?" asked Hugh.

"Flip it over," Raymond said. "I wrote my initials on its underside with a blue marker. RC, same as the cola."

I braced myself for the reckoning, his initials his title of ownership, but when Jim nudged the snapper onto its shell with his tennis shoe, its neck curled like a horseshoe and mouth clamped onto a loose shoelace, its underbelly was free of human marks. I'd been wholly prepared to give the turtle back to Raymond, perhaps receiving commendation for catching it before it could return to the swamp, but he'd lied about tagging it just as I had about where I'd found it – and all, I understood, to let me know he knew I'd stolen it. Maybe he'd even seen me through his kitchen window scampering off with it.

"Told you," he said and winked at me. "Not the same snapper. But it don't matter none. There's plenty more where it came from. You just have to know how to catch 'em."

"Everybody knows how to catch 'em," Jack said. "You see 'em and you pick 'em up, careful not to get a finger bit off in the process."

Everyone snickered, including me. "I mean from the swamp

itself," Raymond said. "With a hook and line. Go get your bikes, I'll show you."

And that's what we did. I put the snapper back in the minnow bucket, set it by the stoop to our kitchen, and the six of us rode on our bikes to the beige duplex at the end of Marshall Street, this so Raymond could gather his tackle. I clung to the rear of our gang so as not to be the first to turn into his driveway and thereby incriminate myself, deluding myself that as long as Raymond kept my secret, I could ignore, and maybe even forget, what I'd done under the spell of jealousy.

At the swamp, our bikes on their sides like deer asleep in the horsetails, Raymond distributed silver five-aught hooks with the solemnity of a priest, then measured out six arm-lengths of nylon kite string. He showed us how to thread the twine through the eyelet, wrap it around the shank, thread it through the loops, and tighten it into a knot that would hold against a turtle's struggle for freedom.

"You bait it like this," he said, dipped his hand into a freezer bag of viscera removed, it seemed, from animals his mother had cleaned in their kitchen, and in his slick palm lay, for all I knew, an eyeball. As he ran a hook through it, careful not to prick his finger, the membranous flesh resisted, gave, and resisted again until the barb burst from the other side like a worm from a grape. He held the baited hook aloft, then twirled the line at his side like a lariat and sent it arcing over the wound-shaped slough. Fluorescent with algae, it languished in the Highway 190 drainage ditch, and through the center of it, thirty feet away, rose the twelve-foot-high chain-linked fence topped with razor wire that surrounded Fort Hood. Raymond's bait plopped just shy of the leaves and trash trapped in it, and the splash rippled outward, jostling lily pads.

"Snappers ain't picky about their cuisine," Raymond said. "They'll eat just about anything. Now go ahead and bait up."

None of us wanted to stick our hands into entrails that lay like an incision in the reeds, but when each of us had, we spread out along the bank and tossed our lines out into the muck. Merle caught the first one. "Bring him in slow and steady," Raymond called to him. Then Jim and Jack and Hugh each caught one. A couple of the snappers were a little bigger than the one I'd stolen, a couple a little smaller, but if all were together in a tank, I wouldn't have been able to tell mine from the others.

And for this I had risked my immortal soul?

In my hospital bed I lay motionless for one day, two days, three, terrified that if I moved at all I'd wind up paralyzed, but also terrified that by remaining still I couldn't know for sure that I wasn't paralyzed already. My father visited before and after his hospital rounds, my mother in the late afternoons pregnant and toting my sister Elaine by the hand, and I was grateful for company that, for fifteen minutes or half an hour, brought relief from the litany of indictments I brought against myself. Except when I had visitors, the nurses who fed me and changed my catheter, the doctors who called me "Sport" and "Champ," I was a spectator at my own trial, I, too, the defendant, prosecutor, judge, and jury, and as much as I wanted to proclaim my innocence, no one knew better than I what I'd done and why.

I imagined growing old without leaving my bed, my arms and legs wizening as they atrophied, whiskers sprouting from my cheeks in adolescence Rip Van Winkling into a beard, eyes wise from what they'd gleaned through windows and television screens, the vicarious experiences of visitors, and the books they'd read to me. I prayed to God for use of my limbs even as I knew all the reasons He had for denying my request and over time I reconciled myself to my fate. If Raymond Calhoun, a boy of eight, had seen through my subterfuge, how could I escape the all-seeing eye of God?

It was then, on the afternoon of the third day, that the doctor who'd performed the lumbar puncture told me that my spine had had the time it needed to heal and it was time for me to move my arms and legs. But by then I had thought about all I would miss in life, the earth and her wonders, the world and its mysteries, and decided that I preferred being quarantined. At least then I would be protected from temptations I couldn't, at seven, even begin to fathom.

I wagged my head, and he said, "See? You're fine." He reminded me that on my nightstand lay comic books, still in their cellophane. "Grab one," he said. "You know you want to." He dangled one in front of me. "It's safe now. You have absolutely nothing to fear."

Kate Angus

FOR YEARS I SAID

I want to die, and what I meant was:

– I'm tired.
– I'm sad.
– I can't believe I did not get that job, that book contract, that idolized beloved's heart to put in my black messenger bag and walk away with.
– I hate this particular body, but there is a version I can imagine loving.
– I don't want to live in any body of any kind.
– There is some fundamental inexplicable way in which I am a failure.

Sometimes I really meant: *I want to sleep for six months or a year* or *I would like to eat ripe Northern Michigan cherries* or *I should sip hot mint*

Kate Angus's non-fiction work has appeared in *The Atlantic Online's* "Object Lessons" series, *Lit Hub, The Rumpus, Los Angeles Review,* and *American Literary Review.* She is also the author of the poetry collection *So Late to the Party* (Negative Capability Books, 2016).

tea so my mouth is a cave of two sensations while Bach's cello suites ache through the radio.

Or I meant: *Can I sit on a white and blue striped towel on the beach while I watch my two children swimming in the ocean?* A boy and a girl, tousle-haired.

I never meant death.

I meant:
All these feelings.

My feelings are little children on a playground when I think of them now. Swinging on the swing set; rappelling across the monkey bars. Sorrow in a blue baseball cap. Joy in a shirt embossed with a tiger. Roar.

My feelings are my only children.

* * *

How is this not a diary? What are these words supposed to do? I tell you the tender green leaves rustled in the wind, thick as water, a wave-sound, and yes the trees are an ocean in the sky outside my second-floor window.

* * *

When I was younger, everything I wrote was about yearning: different lives to wake up in, a future like a closet full of shiny new shoes. A closed closet door now.

* * *

My father was born in 1935. He was 40 when I was born; my mother was 35. I am ten years older than she was when she birthed me, five years older than my father when he first cradled me in his arms.

* * *

All my ancestors die in me every day. All my beloved's ancestors die in me also.

* * *

The Book of Judges claims Abimelech sowed Shechem, his capital, with salt after he put down a rebellion there against him.

The Roman general Acipio Aemilianus plowed Carthage with salt after sacking it during the Third Punic War.

The Duke of Aveiro's palace in Lisbon was taken apart stone by stone and his garden salted so no more greenery or flowers could grow after he took part in a plot to assassinate King Joseph I.

When I search for "who sowed fields with salt?" the Internet replies with a series of other questions:

Is Carthage still salted?
Who salted the fields?
Who salted the land?
Who salted the earth in the Bible?

* * *

Who sowed my womb with salt? Why am I a barren field? Every month, when the basal body thermometer and my cervical fluid tells us, and after I have peed on a paper wand and two thick lines appear like magic, we fuck for four days straight. Whether or not we even want to.

It's been five years and still no baby.

* * *

"After 42," another childless friend says, "the likelihood of getting pregnant naturally is basically zero."

* * *

One friend spent 80K on IVF and now has two children. A friend of a friend and her husband spent 120K and have none. Someone else I know and her now-ex-husband used a surrogate in another state and I dare not imagine that price tag.

* * *

What we did try: fertility acupuncture, fertility self-hypnosis, meditation, royal jelly, maca powder (for him and for her), sea buckthorn, sardines, chasteberry, nettle tea, ubiquinol, a liquid concoction that tastes like hay steeped in alcohol, a particular type of French lubricant I inject into my nether regions with a plastic syringe, torso self-massage.

* * *

I could try to pay for egg retrieval or egg donation or IVF. Some money I've saved sits in my account. But if the fertility treatment works, what money would be left to take care of the baby? Adjuncting pays so little; my partner is three years sporadically employed.

If I become pregnant naturally, we would be broke, but at least then we could feel like it was meant to happen.

And what if we spend the money we meant to retire on trying to conceive and every month I still bleed?

* * *

I first wrote that entire section in the past tense, as if we'd already made our decision and were long past it. Maybe we have. Time makes the decisions if we don't.

I revise it again to change the tense to make it still seem possible. Past tense, present, future: my choice. None of this gives me any power to make a baby happen outside of this page.

* * *

A child pushes a doll in a baby carriage down the street. No, she pushes a kitten dressed up like a doll. Furry little ears, little gray tail.

"I love you," I say to the family dog. "You are my furry baby."

His tongue lolls, his eyes are full of boundless love.

He is my parents' dog. "No," I continue, "you are my furry little brother."

* * *

My tooth hurts. My back hurts. My legs are too tight. My bones carry too much weight. My migraines incapacitate me for days at a time. How could I ever carry a baby to term, how could we ever take care of children?

* * *

"I grow old . . . I grow old.
I shall wear the bottoms of my trousers rolled."

Prufrock and his unattainable women. Not everything is about babies, Kate; not every poem a mirror in which you can see yourself.

* * *

I water the plants. I scrub the tiled floor of the kitchen until it gleams like the hull of a glamorous sci-fi space station. I cook elaborate meals for my parents: cassoulet, duck confit, bo ssam where the pork is wrapped in green lettuce tender as sweet laughter.

I carry the dog with his wounded leg up and down the stairs to recover. I massage my beloved's tight shoulders.

Not every story wraps up with a happy ending.

I want a child. We have no child. Don't tell me all the many other ways to mother.

Debbie Urbanski

THE CAVE

Ian and Tricia Vitkus are not particularly bad White parents. They are not particularly good White parents either. Their White children, Jack and Violet, own excessive amounts of toys. Not all the toys are electronic. Sometimes the children's playthings are made from FSC-certified wood. The entire family is lacto-ovo vegetarian due to environmental and animal-rights concerns. Pigs, sheep, and goats are not necessarily harmed by the family's lifestyle, although the same cannot be said for the dairy cows and egg chickens trapped in industrial organic farming situations in order to produce the cheap rGBH-free milk and cage-free eggs the Vitkuses purchase dirt cheap from Trader Joe's every week. The boy, Jack, was only visibly injured once due to their parenting style, which is a pretty good record. Jack's injury occurred during an incident involving physical guidance that stemmed from the noncompliance of a request and ended with a spectacular contusion also known as a hematoma of tissue across the boy's face. That's as specific as I'm getting. "These

Debbie Urbanski's creative non-fiction has appeared in *Granta, The Sun, Gargoyle, Orion,* and *Terrain.org.* She is also the author of the novel *What Comes After the End* (Pantheon Books, 2022) and many uncollected stories, including several which appeared in *AQR.*

things happen," said their White family therapist, who offered to explain, should Child Protective Services become involved, what Trish had attempted, and failed, to do with her son. I'm pretty sure I already used this anecdote in another story. I like pretending it's something that happened between a fictional mother and a fictional son in a made-up narrative – nothing to do with me! CPS was not called that time though the agency had gotten involved with the Vitkuses years previous, when a White employee at the family print shop, fired recently for incompetency, reported Ian and Tricia for parental negligence. An investigation ensued, the claims were ruled unfounded, case closed, and Jack and Violet continued living with their parents. I don't know if this was necessarily a good idea. Things happen to children. Not all of the things that happen to a child can be good, as you will see later in this story. Now that I think about it, there are two other times Jack's parents facilitated his injury. One involved a hill, a pothole, bicycles, an ambulance, White paramedics, and two White police officers. The other injury took place in a parking lot. This is all part of the background noise. The story I want to tell you, the one about the cave, takes place one nice spring day when the plant material of the forest is still brown, though the snow has melted and the red maples are flowering because those tree species flower earlier than other trees. On that nice day in the spring, the Vitkus family decides to trespass on private land and explore a cave, and something happens to them.

The initial drafts of this story included a lot more background on Trish who, like many of the mothers who populate my fictions, had struggled with depression. *Struggling*, I had written in an early draft, *is a funny word to use, as if Tricia's emotions could be taken down in a wrestling match. Everywhere she looked, she saw a potential, and most likely painful, way to die.* I think I used that last sentence in a different story. Personal secrets offer up such rich source material. Trish planned to kill herself a few days after the cave expedition, I had explained. Her preferred method, popular in Japan at the time, used readily available household cleaning supplies. Fine. I'll tell you. I was depressed myself back then and suicidal and fixated on using that particular Japanese method. A side effect of depression: the inability to get out of your own head. Everything becomes reflective. I'd write a story and in every story there I'd be squatting in the middle of the text, giving myself the finger as I looked for a rope or a blade or a bottle of toilet bowl cleaner to be used as a proton donor when making hydrogen sulfide gas.

Currently my own depression is in remission thanks to a mix of psychotropic medication and a dialectical behavioral therapy skills group, so I've started to wonder if not all my female narrators need be depressed. Already I've erased several sections from this story including the section where Ian doesn't want Trish to tell their kids she's suicidal so she opens the bedroom window and shouts out of the window "I'm SUICIDAL!" and the section where Ian thinks Trish's diagnosis of depression has become an easy way to win an argument, and the section where Trish insists she is claustrophobic so she can't go into a cave and her husband says you have never been professionally diagnosed with claustrophobia, is this another thing you are making up – what a lot of arguing! My husband and I must have been fighting often during the writing of these early drafts – and the section where Trish leaves the house with a handgun in her bag – I'm not sure about the gun, I'll deal with that later – and the section about the suicide notes Trish composes in her head to her daughter and son and husband, and lastly the section that describes, in detail, a recent shopping spree, suicidal planning making Trish stupid with money, where the White cashier at an upmarket outdoors store asks Trish whether she is going on a trip with all these new clothes, and Trish says yes she kind of is.

Forget everything I just told you about Trish's mental state. Here is what actually happens: it's late on a Sunday morning when the Vitkus family buckles into the seats of their hatchback silver Prius. Every Sunday they go on an outing together in order to create a shared experience and reap the documented benefits of outdoor exposure. This Sunday they plan to explore a cave Ian read about on a local adventure forum. Trish, currently a non-depressed mother, remains an undiagnosed claustrophobic. She reminds Ian how she hates the interiors of caves. "Well, I hate not being in a cave," says Ian. Those two can argue about anything. They drive to an urban county park, highway noise filtering through the woods, wads of used toilet paper in the leaf litter. At the informational kiosk, a spray-painted squid stares out at them from a boulder with one enormous dilated eye. There are trees, buzzards. A mile hike along the undulating Faust trail, past numerous White people and speckled dogs, brings them to a junction. They could have chosen either direction. Ian chooses left. They step through the opening in the hemlocks onto private property.

The trees in the new woods are posted KEEP OUT. Violet wants to read every sign. There are many signs. She reads slowly and haltingly, being behind her classmates in reading comprehension. "Violet, honey, it's fine. We aren't going to get in any trouble," Ian says. Violet says, "Property. Hunting. Fishing. Trapping. Trespassing. Strictly. Forbidden. Violators. Will. Be." She says the same thing at the next sign. She says the same thing at the next sign and so forth. They follow a herd path west, not a real trail. On the way to the limestone cliffs, the only people they pass are two White teenagers headed back toward the parking lot. The girl's hair is bleached, her cut-offs frayed, and her faded cropped shirt exposes her stomach. Trish makes judgements based on unconscious biases: the girl looks poor and dumb. The boy's hair looks dirty. "What a beautiful day!" proclaims Ian to the two teens. He has always talked to strangers as if people cared what he thought, a remnant of a wealthy child-hood. "Yeah, really beautiful," says the girl. Below the bluffs is a trailer park with little loops of gray road branching off from the main road. The people down there are so small they don't even count. In six more minutes, the teenagers change direction and will begin to follow Trish and her family at a distance. Something like this actu-ally happened to my family. I've been trying to write this story for three years now. There are decisions that keep needing to be made for the plot to progress and I still don't know what are the right decisions.

"Well here we are," says Ian, dropping his red and blue pack onto the ground and scrambling unencumbered along the rocky outcrop. Violet and Jack follow him like little animals. The drop on the right is 180 feet, I have since read. "You'll die if you fall off there," Trish warns. They don't know where to look for the cave entrance. The in-ternet forums describe this vicinity only in general terms. There had been talk in the forums of "going left on the ridge." The kids leap over fissures. Trish repeats herself. Ian eventually finds the cave no thanks to anybody: a shadowy crevice of rock leading downward. "That's only the beginning part," says Ian, in case anyone considers the entrance unremarkable. Trish considers the entrance to be unre-markable. Near the opening in an aura of damp cold the family en-joys a picnic lunch of hummus, pita, squares of dark chocolate. "Time to go," says Ian, strapping on his helmet. The children strap on their helmets. The cave swallows up Ian, Violet, and Jack in that order. Trish tidies the ground and bags the garbage.

The two teenagers haven't gone away. They stand a hundred feet from the cave entrance discussing a plan. The girl laughs. An ugly laugh or is that Trish using her social stereotypes to be judgmental again? Judgy Trish decides to settle down beside a maple tree and read. She removes a book from her bag, a narrative non-fiction ac-count by a White author about the opioid epidemic, specifically about White mothers who lose their White teenagers to overdoses. The boy, the girl drift closer, kicking at the dull green moss. Trish looks up from her book and smiles in their direction. She looks so stupid smiling like that. This behavior of hers has something to do with the recent 2016 presidential election. The anger and fear of that election made Trish determined to understand those who held different opinions from her or came from different backgrounds. Is now the time to bring up with Trish that smiling does not equal understanding? Another White child dies in the book from an overdose, and the teenage boy offers Trish a little wave of his left hand before striding into the woods up a tree-lined slope, a red and blue hiking bag slung over his shoulder OH MY GOD is that Ian's backpack? Is the teenage boy stealing Ian's backpack? Is that what this story is about, a fucking backpack that gets taken from some middle-class White hikers who still have three more bags sitting there on the detritus –

People lose much more all the time.

I want to tell this story anyway. Is that okay?

The criminal possibilities for what happened to my family that day are petty theft, grand theft, and perhaps robbery. To determine the correct crime, I first need to find the value of what was taken from us. Then I need to figure out whether violence (or threat of violence) was used on us. That red and blue pack bouncing on the sturdy back of the teenage boy belonged to my husband, a technical hiking bag made by the German brand Deuter, whose CEO is White and whose web site features photographs of White people enjoying the outdoors. Inside the pack had been my son's pullover, a discontinued style, the only long-sleeve he would wear. Also: the Sunday's *New York Times*, a Nalgene bottle, a pricy filter that kills water-borne bacteria with UV light, a first-aid kit, a feeling of security, a cover I had thrown over a memory, four Kind bars, and a deck of cards. They took my daughter's walking stick. We spent a long and frantic time wandering the woods searching for the missing items. My daughter cried and cried. I am going to call what we experienced *grand theft* because the act did not feel petty to my daughter or to me. The question of violence or the threat of violence will be addressed later on in this story.

The teenage girl continues to saunter lazily along the rocks in Trish's direction. Below them, in the cliff's shadow, a fight ensues at the trailer park: two White girls on the ground on a patch of grass beside a singlewide throw punches, kicks. The girls are play-acting or else they're getting hurt. Jack's White second nanny lived in a trailer home. The second nanny prayed a lot, was a know-it-all, eventually needed knee surgery. That's all Trish knows about these sorts of communities. Then maybe you shouldn't include trailer homes in your story, Trish, I want to tell her. The problem being that the trailer homes are already there. If she or I pull them out of the story, we can cause a rockslide. Besides, there really is a trailer park beneath the cave. I'm not making this up. 3.3 stars on Google. "A lot of clutter," says one reviewer. By this point the teenage girl, having reached Trish, is standing close to her, standing over her in fact while chewing on a piece of cheap purple gum. Different societal groups hold different expectations around personal space, Trish reminds herself, pretending to feel comfortable and curious and so friendly there on the cliff. "What are you guys doing out here?" Trish asks, using a casual voice as if the two of them are having a conversation. "We're trespassing," the girl replies. "What about you?"

What actually happened: I was sitting outside the cave into which my children and my husband had recently entered when a White girl in her later teens wearing an unflattering half-shirt walked up to me and stood very close to me, and while she was standing there close to me, I made a series of assumptions about her, which is not a really nice thing to do. I did it anyway. I assumed she was lower class and she voted for Trump or her parents did and she didn't like people from other countries and she was racist and xenophobic and homophobic and ignorant and only spoke one language and had previously gotten into some trouble. She must have made assumptions about me too. Sample assumptions about me: that I am middle-aged, irrelevant, an easy target, a privileged hypocrite, I voted for Clinton and had an easy life. Some of those assumptions would be correct. It felt like she was guarding me but not in a protective way. I think she was guarding me while her boyfriend ran back to the parking lot carrying my husband's backpack. I wonder what she would have done had I noticed the backpack missing. I didn't notice the backpack was missing. I noticed she was standing so close to me. Uncomfortable with her nearness, I became uncomfortable with my discomfort and made myself say hello. She said hello. After that, I pretended she wasn't there. After that, I pretended she was there. While I pretended she was either there or not there, this story idea started playing in my mind about a mother – a depressed mother? – who meets a teenage girl – wearing a half shirt? – in an isolated part of the woods above a trailer park – why do I keep mentioning the trailer park like it's some shocking yet important detail? – and they have a conversation, the mother pretending to be super relaxed while also aware of the potential violence of their isolation. The mother's awareness turns out to be prescient as the teenager in the story ends up attacking the mother in the story, and since I am the mother in the story, you know what that means, I, in the story, get brutally attacked, then the girl and her teenage boyfriend who had returned attack my family and we all die or only the mother dies or only one of the children. Does me imagining violence count as actual violence or a threat of violence? Because it certainly felt real. For the rest of that day and several days after, I felt like I had physically been mugged. My husband kept saying to our kids, "Kids, keep an eye on Mom. She thinks she's been mugged!" Someone once called my imagination "fabulous." My husband thinks, in addition to depression, I have anxiety. So does my East Indian primary care doctor. I feel like a lot of people are worried these days. Back at the cave, I took out my cell phone in what I hoped was a casual manner. There was no signal. Casually I put my cell phone away. Casually I shouted my husband's name. "Hey! H.! Time to go!" I leaned into the cave entrance and shouted his name. There wasn't an answer. I pretended to read and pretended to turn my narrative nonfiction book's increasingly panicked pages. This teenage girl was reminding me in an unpleasant way of these other two White teenage girls who, years ago, mugged me in the quiet or some might say deserted residential neighborhood beside my undergraduate college campus one spring night. I think the technical term is *robbed*. Their similarly pudgy stomachs, long hair, not all that pretty, dumb eyes. I shouldn't describe people that way. *Simplifying their characters*, I wrote on an earlier draft of this story in aqua lagoon ink. But that's really how I saw them, and when I saw them like that, that's really who they became. They had both spent a lot of time on their hair and wore black eyeliner applied thickly.

Here is what happened: the two girls had been following me for several blocks in the irregularly lit dark. They were behind me and ran toward me. I heard the increase of their footfalls. I turned around. They stopped running. I turned back around and started walking. They ran toward me. I turned around. They stopped running. I didn't want to offend them by asking them, "Why are you following me?" So I said, "Hi." They said, "Hi." I turned around and started walking. One of the girls pushed me down and demanded my money. The girl's dialogue sounded like a bad line from a play. I got up and started walking. The girl grabbed me, the other girl punched me in the face. A blank space of time exists between the girl drawing back her arm, her face so focused and intent, and I see her fist then nothing then all the blood. I was so surprised. In my wallet, a $20 bill. I was a college student on work study with federally subsidized loans and Pell grants and no disposable income. They took my $20 and ran away like someone was going to chase them down. For a long time after, I was always crossing to the other side of the street, like my mother had taught me, only in her examples, it was a lone man walking toward me dangerously. She also told me to lock the car doors and roll up the windows when driving through a Black neighborhood. I don't tell a lot of people this story. There is still residual embarrassment. "*Girls?*" I was asked with a giggle.

What actually happened: Trish is certain the girl is watching her. Yet whenever she glances up from her non-fiction narrative book about the opioid crisis, the girl pretends to be so busy digging the dirt out from her fingernails or kicking tiny pebbles over the cliff edge. Enough, Trish finally decides. She checks her watch. She makes a big deal about her watch checking, using wide gestures, audibly murmuring about the impermanence of time, where did the day go. "Hey Ian!" Trish shouts. She leans over the opening to the cave shouting Ian's name again. No response. The girl besides Trish laughs. "What are you laughing at?" Trish asks, scooting closer to her bag, which is vibrating with a bright and wary, or waxy?, energy – okay, excuse me, but before the story progresses any further, I need to figure out whether there is a gun in Trish's bag.

The benefits of adding a gun to Trish's bag includes variation and uncertainty: who will shoot whom, will it be a hit or a miss, will it be a fatal or superficial injury, are the police involved, does an ambulance arrive. On the other hand, I know very little about guns myself other than what I learned online when I was depressed and researching how to shoot myself in the right temple or the rear base of my head which is a more reliable spot but also less specific. On the other hand, I could research guns on Google and visit a local gun shop. If Trish owned a gun, I could weave issues of gun violence and ownership throughout the plot. I am aware these days how it's easier to publish a story when the story touches upon larger societal issues. Gun violence is a larger societal issue. Motherhood is not, I need to keep reminding myself. But a mother with a gun –

The girl laughs again. "I don't think you should be laughing right now," says Trish toughly. She reaches for her bag and inside her bag she grips the gun that Ian made her buy after she got mugged by a pack of teenage girls. Ian had driven her to the local gun shop the day after the mugging. They brought the children. They did not bring the children. The children were either there or not there. "I'm not going to shoot a high school girl," Trish had argued with Ian at the time. "I'm not saying you shoot the girl in the head," Ian had said. "Do you want something that will fit in your purse?" asked the White gun salesman. "I consider purses to be stupid," said Trish. "What do you carry then?" asked the salesman. "A small tote," said Trish. Her face was still swollen and distorted. One of the girls had punched her in the nose then again in the side of her head. "I think you would do well with this model," said the salesman, removing a handgun from the glass display case. He cupped the gun in his hands and explained, "This solid lightweight pistol features a high-strength polymer frame with an ergonomic grip, plus a double action fire control, manual thumb safety, two magazines, stainless steel drift adjustable sights, external takedown lever and slide stop. Backed by a lifetime service policy – "

I'm not sure this is working. Let me try a different approach.

Here is what actually happens: Jack is sitting on the rock and watching as his father and sister and eventually even his anxiety-prone mother descend into the cave. "Don't worry. We will all be fine," murmurs Trish before dropping out of view, never mind she is too middle-aged to be dropping in and out of caves, never mind the questionable ethics of trespassing or the teenagers lurking in the periphery. Jack is staying behind because I have no idea actually. Probably he wanted to go in the cave too. He was like, "Why the heck am I not going in the cave?" I'm sorry, Jack, I need someone to stay above ground. I already tried the mother; there wasn't enough tension. "It's not a real cave anyway," Jack tells himself, as real caves have gift shops and restrooms. He pulls a book from his bag and begins to read a graphic novel about a boy who lives in a small city. Around Jack there are the bare trees, the vultures, the teenagers admiring the elevated view of the interstate, a pile of the Vitkus family bags. Ian's bag is already missing. Trish's tote on the top of the pile contains a gun. The teenage girl moves closer as the steep angles of the rock signify foreboding.

"Your parents sure are stupid to leave you here," says the girl. Jack turns the page of the book. It is a book in which nothing much happens. The boy, the city – he turns the page again. He turns the page again. The girl snatches his book away and holds it out of reach. "What'd they do, did they leave you here? Some parents."

"They didn't leave me," says Jack. "They're in the cave."

"They didn't leave me here," repeats the girl mimicking Jack's little voice. I was going to say she tosses Jack's book off the cliff but this seems an overly aggressive action so early in the scene. Instead let's have the girl return the book to Jack by throwing it hard at his chest. Actually the girl likes to read. That's irrelevant. During this interaction, the girl's companion, her boyfriend, can be seen jogging up a wooded hill in the distance toward the parking lot. On the boy's back: the missing red and blue backpack.

"That's my dad's bag," says Jack, pointing.

"I don't think so," says the girl.

Jack looks around. "Then where did my dad's bag go?"

"Your dad never had a bag, silly," says the girl. "Anyway, you still have your own bag, right? Don't be a greedy reedy." She leans against the tree and stretches her neck to the left, to the right. I was about to say that next, in a series of rapid movements, this girl grabs Jack by the arms and hurls him off the cliff to increase the story's tension, but on further examination, it is less a cliff and more a series of ledges. Anyway, she doesn't yank Jack by the arms. Her hair falls into her eyes. She jerks her hair out of her eyes and stretches her neck again. She isn't that flexible. "What's your name anyway?"

"I'm not telling you."

"Well my name's Mindy. That's not my real name but you have to call me that from now on."

"Okay."

"Okay, *Mindy*. Now you say it." The rocks they sit on are hard and uneven. In the cracks of the rocks, thin layers of dirt accumulate slowly over a period of years. In particularly fertile cracks, there are maple seedlings. None of the seedlings are going to make it. The girl selects a pointed rock from the ground and aims the rock at Jack's forehead. Jack says the girl's fake name. "Good job. What's inside your dad's bag anyway?"

"My hoodie. I'm cold." Mindy removes her sweatshirt from around her waist and gives it to Jack, who won't take it. "Take it," she orders. "It's a girl's shirt," Jack says. She throws her shirt at the boy. It smells like a fire. "You put that on," Mindy says. "It gets cold up here and you don't want to get cold. Once you get cold, it's hard to warm up again." She nudges Jack with the tip of her dirty white athletic shoe. Jack puts on the sweatshirt. It looks like he is wearing a girl's sweatshirt. "So do you want to go in the cave?" she asks. "No," says Jack. "What if I made you? What if I pushed you down that hole?" she asks. Jack leans over his book until his forehead nearly touches the pages. Large birds circle above them in uneven circles. I used to say "large black birds," but that description felt ethically suspect in a story with no Black people as of yet. More about that later. Jack is close to crying. "Hey, I'm joking. Come on. It's just talk. We're just talking." Mindy jokingly grabs the book out of Jack's hands again. This time she reads the book out loud to him, giving each character a different funny voice. Soon Jack is laughing at the appropriate parts and the sun produces wider fatter shadows of the trees. On the interstate, a semi hauls an unmarked trailer south. Mindy has completed the reading of two chapters and is halfway through a third when her boyfriend returns. He carries a stick over his shoulder. "About time," says the girl and she tosses the book to the ground and gets up to leave.

"We're not leaving yet," says the boy, smiling, his hands wrapped loosely around the stick. "I have to meet this kid's family first."

"I don't think you need to meet his family," says the girl.

"In fact, I think this boy should come with me to meet his family. You come with me," he says, pointing to Jack. A plane flies overhead, gaining altitude. The white contrails dissipate. Jack tips his head back and watches the plane.

"He's, what, eight years old. He doesn't have to come with you," Mindy says. She steps between the boy and Jack and sticks out her wet pink tongue at the boy and wags her tongue around.

The boy laughs, shrugs. "Ready or not," he says but not loudly. Scrambling down the crevice by himself, he is underground for a long time. Mindy picks up the book again. She grows tired of the book, of the view, the boy.

"What's taking that asshole so long?" She glances at Jack. "Do you know what *asshole* means?" Jack says yes, he knows. "Good. I don't want to have to explain it to you." There isn't a breeze. Her hair hangs limply past her shoulders. "Can I have my book?" Jack asks. Mindy hands him his book. Jack turns the pages. He turns another page. "You don't want to be here after dark," says Mindy. "This place is haunted. Weird shit comes out of the rocks after dark. Not ghosts," she explains. "Ghosts are stupid. This shit coming out from the rocks is real. It feels your neck and the inside of your mouth. Plus something's living in the cave so you have to be careful." Jack isn't listening to her. She wiggles her fingers and jabs her hand into his neck. He squeals. She didn't mean to do it so hard. I had meant earlier in the scene to describe some black ants – should I change the ants to red? Remove the color altogether? Keep the color but note my hesitation? – emerging from their winter dormancy, crawling languidly across the rocks, but before I can go ahead and do this the older boy emerges from the cave, huffing from the climb. He doesn't have the stick anymore. "Some parents you have," laughs the boy, shaking his head.

"We have to go now." Mindy tugs the older boy's arm.

"Where's my dad's backpack?" asks Jack.

"What are you talking about? Are you talking about my backpack?" says the older boy.

"I thought we went over this already," says Mindy.

"I put my backpack in my *car*," the boy says.

Mindy starts clapping. "Your car," she says, clapping some more. She leans in toward Jack. "Don't you be stupid too," she whispers. Her breath smells. The teenagers go off running and laughing into the woods. The boyfriend falls. Mindy helps him up. They keep running.

When Jack can't see them anymore, he removes the girl's sweatshirt though he keeps it on his lap in case she comes back. She doesn't come back and he throws the sweatshirt off the cliff. He had hoped the wind would catch the terrycloth material, that the shirt would sail off in a northern direction like a migratory bird. The sweatshirt behaves in a realistic manner. A handgun remains in Trish's bag but nobody bothered in the previous scene to look in the bag which has toppled over into the invasive underbrush etc. This gun plotline still seems very silly. Unless Jack goes over to the bag now and gets the gun out of the bag and shoots – himself? Now that would be a bleak story. He shoots a bird. He shoots at me? I should just take away the gun. I remove the gun from Trish's bag and return it to the display case at the gun shop. Now in the tote: a bag of unsalted nuts, a pocket pack of Kleenex, a pad of paper, a ballpoint pen, a deck of cards, Chapstick, bottled water, a change purse, an empty wrapper, children's chewable ibuprofen – essentially everything that was in Trish's bag before is there now other than the gun. The contents of the remaining bags remain unchanged.

I'm supposed to be working on this story again. It's a new decade. Instead of working on this story, I'm texting with my White friends and my one East Indian friend. We want to talk about the civil unrest. One friend says she plans to attend a local protest. Another friend says she purchased a book on anti-racism for her children. She tossed the book onto the sofa so her kids can discover it themselves. Another friend is crying and can't stop crying. I don't have any Black friends. I haven't cried much since I started taking the fluoxetine and bupropion prescribed by my East Indian psychiatrist in 2017. Before the meds, I cried every day for years. I wish I could say I had been crying all that time for racial injustice. That's not why I was crying. There has been an increase in both fireworks and gunshots in the city.

I live in a mostly White area. By "mostly" I mean one Black family resides on this three-block street. For years we had frequent break-ins in the neighborhood, the police force called them "crimes of opportunity," high schoolers taking advantage of windows or doors left unlocked. For us, it was a broken lock on our back door. My husband had planned to fix the lock someday but he had other priorities hence the teenager who broke into our house. The teenager opened every kitchen drawer while my children and my husband and I were asleep upstairs. When I entered the kitchen the next morning, every drawer hung open. I wish he would have shut the drawers. Technically this was a burglary. He broke into several other homes that night as well. According to another homeowner's security footage, he removed his shoes before walking inside. I am uncomfortable that this kid who broke into our house was Black. I am uncomfortable that his parents are war refugees. Previously he had been in trouble but at a younger age. The police asked my husband if he wanted to press charges. If we pressed charges – or my neighbors pressed charges – he, now 16 years old, would be tried as an adult. That was the law back then. I realize he is the first Black individual to enter my story. I feel self-conscious about this fact, anxious. I am not supposed to Google things when writing to maintain my focus but, in light of the recent protests, I allow myself to Google how a White author can write about race. Options: don't identify any character's race. Identify every character's race. Do not assume, or think a reader should assume, that characters with undefined races are automatically White.

Any of this is reasonable.

Excuse me while I return to the beginning of this story and label the race of every one of my characters.

I don't know what to do with the color of the ants, the birds.

My husband told the cops he wanted to press charges. I thought it would be more of a discussion topic, like what is our responsibility as White people to this child of war refugees who broke into our house? Eventually we got our iPads back though it took a long time as the iPads were considered evidence. I remember finding items belonging to my family scattered around the block that day. I think the teenage boy may have taken an expensive waterproof running jacket of mine with revolutionary membrane construction. There is the chance that I lost the jacket myself. More advice: do not have the only Black characters in your story be criminals. This seems like common sense yet look what I'm doing. Should I go back and make my psychiatrist Black or my family therapist Black? The problem being my psychiatrist and family therapist are not Black. The problem being I know very few Black people personally. It was a different situation in Minneapolis where I used to live. My boss in Minneapolis had been Black, and her boss was Black, and my other boss was Black along with many of my coworkers. Please tell me this makes me a better person. Plus my daughter did once have a Black friend before she moved away. Part of me was glad she moved away. I was so uncomfortable talking to the Black girl's Black mother. Everything I said contained multiple and unintentional meanings.

Since our break-in, our cars have been rummaged through multiple times, most recently last week. We're becoming used to it, part of the city living experience. People who lock their car doors get their windows smashed. Certain neighbors installed private exterior cameras to record everyone who approaches. I want one of those cameras. My husband says now don't be ridiculous. Let me tell you a story. One morning several months after the 2016 election my doorbell rang. The ringing continued for a full minute which does not sound like a long time now but it felt like a long time in that moment. I ignored the ringing. Nobody rings the doorbell anymore unless they are selling something. There was nothing I wanted to buy right then. The ringing changed to knocking. More like pounding. The pounding on the front door went on for a longer time. I was in the attic working. I crept to the half-moon windows to peer outside. The angle was unfortunate: I had no way to view the front doorway. There had been additional break-ins in my neighborhood and reported incidents of house casings. The suspects were generally late teens, generally Black, often male though not always, wearing outfits such as "a black hooded jacket with white writing on the left chest area." One possibility is racial paranoia. But those private security cameras recorded the suspects breaking into a house, so it's not like this was entirely made up. The community was asked to report suspicious activity to their neighborhood police. I realize how this sounds. White people calling the police on Black people. What a bad idea. I am not being sarcastic. *I just have never seen this person in the neighborhood before*, someone wrote on our neighborhood watchlist describing *a tall thin Black male wearing one of those black skull caps* who potentially was casing her house or else looking to pick up a sink discarded at the curb. Or else both casing and wanting the sink. Had I remembered to lock the door this morning? Another incident from the watchlist: *Early this afternoon, our front doorbell rang. A Black female, about 15 years old, asked for a "Samantha Lynn." I told her that that person does not live here and peppered her with questions. In short, Samantha Lynn is supposedly her stepsister, yet her home address is unknown. Clearly, she was casing our house. I called 911 to report a suspicious person and the girl, seeing me on the phone through a front window, walked quickly away, turning east on M – Drive. I drove up and down R – Avenue, but did not see her. When I returned home, a police officer was waiting to take a statement. He said that other officers were searching the neighborhood, but I doubt she was found.* If we hear actual intruders enter our houses, we have been told not to confront them. We have been told to call 911 and vacate the premises. From my attic the only way out is through the skylight windows onto the roof or down a flight of stairs then another flight of stairs which leads to the front door. I made a point of saying hello whenever one of the Black kids from the public high school who didn't live on my block walked down my block. I wanted them to feel welcome walking down my block. At the same time, I had begun to look at people I didn't know with suspicion. The pounding on my front door continued long after it was appropriate. I switched off the lights and, in the natural dimness, remained very still. When I was a child, my father slept with a gun under his pillow in order to protect us. That's how the story goes anyway. We lived in the glossy Chicago suburbs then. We had moved out of the city in the early '80s, my parents charmed by pictures of the new suburban developments with names like *Pinewood East* and *Heritage Estates.* Black people had begun to move into our city neighborhood on the South Side anyway, which was lowering the housing values. My mother says it was more the good suburban schools that made her want to leave. Our new suburban development happened to not have any Black people in it or around it. In middle school my father purchased my family's first alarm system also for our own protection. The alarm system felt excessive in that setting. No one unknown had ever walked down our suburban street. I should have felt safe in my childhood, with the gun, with the alarm system. In high school, my dad gifted me a pocket-size container of mace. Also in high school, my mother took me to a self-defense seminar where we made weapons out of our car keys and practiced poking out a male assailant's eye. The pounding on the front door stopped. The doorbell started up again. Can you remember, in the months after the election, the political violence in the air around this time? The suggestion that people we didn't recognize had the hearts of criminals. I didn't believe it all. On my knees I crawled to the windows again. Nobody was on my street. That's the end of the story. I wonder if I should go back and change the races of my characters. Am I still allowed to do that? If I am allowed to do that, who should be Black and who should be White? There are a lot of new rules. Of course there are.

Question: Is it possible for me to say anymore, *I am not going to bring race into a story?*

Answer: No.

Question: Is not mentioning the race of the characters a racial decision?

Answer: Yes.

Question: Can I just tell the truth, how it happened?

Answer: No.

We walk back and forth for a long time in the woods looking for what we are afraid of. The problem being that we are not all afraid of the same thing. I worry I am writing this story in the wrong genre. Let me try again. Apologies for the sudden transition in literary style but I do want to tell you what really happened at the cave.

Trish: Hi.

Teenage girl: Hi.

Trish: Hey, that's my husband's hiking bag.

Teenage girl: Yeah, it is.

Trish: Give me back the bag.

Teenage girl: No.

Trish: I'm going to call the police. [pulls out her phone from her pocket]

Teenage girl: Yeah, right. There's no signal here.

Trish: Ian! Ian? IAN!

Teenage girl: Shut up. [leaning in toward the cave.] What the fuck is that noise?

Here is what happens. There's this glutinous monster in the cave. A monster with no eyes, a ragged mouth, large, that captures scent molecules by waving around coarse hairs on its roughened trans-lucent skin. This monster is not a metaphor for depression or racial injustice or climate change or right-wing authoritarianism. This monster is a monster and what everybody, all along, should have been afraid of. Possessive, cranky, ferocious, sensitive, ignored, the monster first eats Ian and Violet entirely but it only eats a part of Jack, a small part, so Jack crawls out of the cave missing a portion of his left foot. This is so scary! He emerges from the cave in pain and shock, his foot spurting blood. Squinting into the sunlight, he sees his mother and a teenage girl wrestling at the bluff's edge. He says there is a monster coming. Trish says if there's a monster coming, what are they going to do about that. The monster emerges. The girl lets go of Trish's arms. "Shit," says the girl. Jack dies after the monster eats more of him. The girl dies. Trish dies. They probably deserved it. I'm thinking of the food chain, the efficient transfer of energy, the tertiary consumers. When the teenage boy returns, monster and bod-ies and body parts have retreated into the cave. Though there are still remnants on the ground. The heel of a shoe. An ear. Innards. The boy gets out of there, sprints back to the parking lot, screeches into town in Ian's silver Prius which has such lousy acceleration. He goes to the bagel shop where his friends work and tells some story about a monster who lives in the cave and eats people. I'd be lying if I said nobody went into the cave again after hearing such a story. People go into the cave. They think it's fun to be scared. The monster eats those people up. The county seals off the cave's entrance with sturdy wooden boards. People remove the wooden boards, wanting to prove they aren't scared, that there is no such thing as a monster. The problem being there is such a thing as a monster. These people get eaten up too. It's popular these days to tell a story from the monster's point of view, to explain its personal history and motivations, to show that "bad" and "good" are value judgements we make based on our own biases. That's a different story than the story I'm telling. A foul smell lingers near the opening. "Oh, it's only a smell," someone says. "There's nothing to be afraid of."

LONG POEMS

Alison Hawthorne Deming

FIELD STUDIES
Bowdoin College Scientific Station
Kent Island, New Brunswick, Canada

1. First, There Was an Albatross

Ernest Joy spotted the bird
lost or adventuring from
south of the equator, spied it
flying offshore from Wood Island
yellow-nosed albatross
rare in the North and close enough
to shoot as naturalists in his day
did so numerous were the furred
and feathered and finned. Joy gave
the bird to Allan Moses, island naturalist,
skilled at taxidermy who knew
the Museum of Natural History
would want the skin for study
and so traded it for passage
on a Congo expedition hunting
Grauer's green broadbill, a gap
in the museum's collection.
The team crossed Lake Tanganika,
traversed the plateaus of Marungu,
sailed north to Uvira, trekked
by foot with a caravan of porters
to the forest of the Upper Congo.

Alison Hawthorne Deming is the author of seven poetry collections, most recently *Stairway to Heaven* (Penguin Poets, 2016). She has four essay collections, most recently *A Woven World: On Fashion, Fishermen, and the Sardine Dress* (Counterpoint Press, 2021). Her work has appeared widely in journals and anthologies, including *The Norton Book of Nature Writing* and *The Best American Science and Nature Writing*.

Moses found the bird feeding
on berries in a vine-draped tree
while others were off in the bush.
They returned to find Moses asleep
in his tent, grass green broadbill
lying dead on his chest. With what
satisfaction, they wrote, we proceeded
to dissection! Moses complained.
All this for one dead bird? (935 birds
to be exact.) Will you do nothing,
he complained to his sponsor,
for the eiders back home on Kent Island?
Mere finger of grassy meadow and
rocky shore safe enough for nesting.
The albatross knew nothing of this
human story. It had flown
and when it fell made history.

2. Navigation of the Leach's Storm Petrel

Science wanted to know
what they know, sooty little
tube-nosed ocean runner,
fork-tailed forest-burrower,
night wanderer, transient in
the sweet musk of woods.
How do their find their way?
What's their sense of place?
Do they know a sense of
belonging when they return
from a year at sea to breed
in the forest where they hatched?
Or is just work to repair the burrow?
They stagger around at night
on forest paths. They don't
understand the land
but they need it. A man
who studied the colony
for half a century took a few
petrels to Ireland to see
if they could find the way

back. First bird got back
before the man. Was it
nine days or thirteen?
Do the numbers matter
when the bird just knew,
its inner compass reading
longitude and latitude, skirting
open ocean swells to arrive
exactly where it knew it should be?

3. Site Fidelity of the Leach's Storm Petrel

At night the pairs chuckle and purr
sometimes in harmony
nestled in their burrows
ghosting the forest with
their chatter. They have a lot
to say after spending so long
in solitary flight with nothing
on their minds but light
and wind and the scent of prey
that draws them onward.
They might fly four hundred
kilometers from land
seeking lanternfish and krill,
loading oil to bring home
for the chick. They winter
at sea, Newfoundland
to Equator, intimate only
with water until some brain
or body switch flips.
Who can explain the call
for another, the call for home?
Together again, same time,
same place, next year,
more faithful to burrow
than to spouse, grooming
the nest with soft leaves,
fresh grass, they talk
and talk throughout the night.

4. Petrel Chick

What did I know
lying in the darkness
where I had hatched?
At first I loved the smell
of loam, musk, the dampness
of the underneath. Then came
a fishy scent though
what did I know of fish?
Bill to bill my lunch
was served. I had no
control over where
I lived, when or what
I ate. But sufficient
to my status as a puff
of proto-feathers the meals
kept tunneling down
from the spot of light
at burrow's end. I knew
to raise my mouth
to what arrived.
I had no idea what I was
or what I was meant to be.
Ridiculous, I know, that
I should have a voice.
Sleep and eat and roll over
in the earthen dark
that was life until
I grew so blubbered
I could barely turn in my sleep.
I squeezed out of that earthhold
when I caught the open ocean scent
that told me I had wings
and I was gone into
sea-spangled spume and sky.

5. Parent-Offspring Conflict

We take turns leaving the nest
to forage, one fasting
the other flying as far

as it takes, Georges Bank
or Cape Cod, to gorge
on krill for the little one
and the mate we've left behind.
Sometimes out there
in the beyond with no
markers of time and place
it just feels right to keep going
the forest burrow, a bother
all duty and constraint.
Besides we live so long
we barely age at all.
Telomeres, biologists say,
fragment as they age.
Not ours. So what
does it matter if this year
one bird does not go back?
There will be more chicks
and more. Some years
we get out there in the grey
where the sea and the sky mix
and the land—what is land?
This year it's all about flight.

6. Floral Constancy of the Bumblebee

Flowers because they are grounded
in the earth have an electric field
around them, the biologist says,
fact becoming poem. Her work
to study how bumblebees learn
what flowers to visit for nectar.
Transects map the pollinator
network of the island. Leafcutters,
she says, make sleeping bags
from circles they cut from rose leaves.
Sweat bees, she says, favor
Queen Anne's lace. If you are a bee,
she says, visiting hawkweed,
yellow rattle, dewberry, milkweed,
blueberry, clover and vetch
you need to learn with each flower

how to get down into the sweet.
But if you specialize on one
blossom shape you can get
right down to business.
A good plan, she says,
because it takes a while to learn
how to handle a flower.

7. Learning in the Savannah Sparrow

Bird brain, we humans say,
to put someone down. But try
making a nest in the grass
on an isolated northern archipelago,
raising your chicks in the open
where gulls and ravens prey.
Try flying on the power of your
thin feathered arms to spend winter
in a southern clime a thousand miles away
then flying back to the same meadow
to mate, knowing how to avoid
close relatives for pairing,
the whole cycle playing like
an earworm year after year,
and each summer learning the song
the meadow is singing and carrying
that tune with you wherever you go.

8. Fog Heaven

Being a matter
of numbers and vials
the cloud physicist
found it
easy to live
in a cabin the size of
a heavy stillness
that wants
to dissipate.
He mastered the art
of bottling fog.

I slept with his ashes
perched on a shelf
no one ready
to let him go.
But the stars
kept waking me
or was it
the ghost asleep
in the corner
wrapped in tin foil
and lush night
upon me like
moss on a forest log.

NOTES

"First, There was an Albatross" is a title borrowed from Nathaniel Wheelright's 2014 article in *Bowdoin Magazine* telling the story of Ernest Joy's discovery of the albatross near Grand Manan Island and the establishment of the Bowdoin College Scientific Research Station. J. Sterling Rockefeller wrote in *The Auk: Ornithological Advances* in 1933 about the expedition to the Congo to find Grauer's Green Broadbill. Rockefeller did in fact do something for the nesting eiders. He purchased Kent Island and donated it to Bowdoin College as a refuge for birds. In 1954 Chuck Huntington began his research on the Leach's storm petrels that nest in burrows on Kent. His work continued for 50 years. His obituary states that he "amassed longitudinal data on a single population of animals over an interval and at a level of detail that are perhaps without equal in field biology." The work continues with ornithologists Bob Mauck and Mark Hauseman. An article by John M. Pearce on the philopatry (site faithfulness) of the petrel was published in *The Auk* in 2007. Nathaniel Wheelright has led research on Savannah sparrows. Patty Jones, current Director of the Field Station, conducts the work on the nectaring behavior of bees. Robert Cunningham, cloud physicist at MIT, came to the island in 1938 to study fog. He slept in a tiny cabin named Fog Heaven. The data he collected helped lead to the U.S. Clean Air Act of 1970. He painstakingly gathered data on Kent for 60 years. This sequence of poems, then, is something of a collaboration with a community of scientists who have devoted their working lives to learning what one remote little island in the Bay of Fundy had to teach us.

Bruce Bond

DOVE OF THE MORNING NEWS

Click on Pierre Teilhard de Chardin,
and you find a man whose Christ has a body,
and that body is not finished growing.

The surface of modern earth lies below
a glow of talk and optic fiber, the angel
of our noosphere, engorged and breathing,

metastasized into intelligent machines,
the throes of fevers arcing our backs,
contagions of our traffic raised, curved,

shuttled through the crossed emergent roar
of light. You see what de Chardin saw,
our circuits cast in one great nervous system

of the whole, flags of contrails flowing over
cities, the blood of strangers into streams
of smoke that flood the boundaries we call strange.

* * *

What is the will to live if not the means
and meaning of the bridge, what if not
a common fire beneath the stanchions,

the sharp green scent of a burst of rain.
Yesterday my wife fainted in the market.
She shattered her bottles, broke her jaw,

Bruce Bond is the author of twenty-eight books of poetry, most recently *Invention of the Wilderness* (LSU, 2022). His work has appeared widely in journals and anthologies, including seven editions of *The Best American Poetry*.

and the many strangers rushed to her
to offer her bandages, an ambulance call,
the wordless reparation of her groceries.

Without the mask or glove of our season,
an old man knelt in his boy-blue super-
market vest, and she said, *thank you, please,*

do not touch me. She can feel it still,
that hand. When she lies down, it lies down
beside her. Like a beast beside a child.

* * *

What good is our proximity to heaven
if it sends no word. Only the winds
of Chernobyl over northern Europe,

the air that binds, that empties what it fills,
fevers the autumns of New England
like a plague. What you cannot see

you see in the eyes of the paralyzed,
the drift of the garbage, the uplifted
hair and banners on the White House lawn.

You hear it in our cattle like a train
to somewhere, though no one says just where.
And you know it will not last, the air

for the taking, but you were born to it,
for the cry to clear your lung of spit
and blood, to search for the right words to breathe.

* * *

After bombs beat the many precincts
of our town to cinders, the charred bricks
stood in jagged monoliths or scattered

across the roads that carried us survivors
by foot. In search of what, hard to tell,
the living, the dead, the unknown neighbor.

After the weary initiation of repairs,
as the wreckage cooled and peace received
its signatures, a chill swept over us,

a shared sense of what we suffered, lost,
what we saw in the random casualty.
The deep sensation of the irrevocable

haunted small greetings among strangers.
Blood banks drained, and filled, and filled again.
When one eye shuddered, so too another.

* * *

The earth below the throat is paradise,
said a child of the age of permission,
and I worried, and then, he died

of the shame and sacrament he drank,
alone, divided against the voice that says,
you can love a heaven and hate its god.

You can vacate the house and chronic
rancor of your childhood and pause,
look up, hypnotized beneath the white

glass of trees, not knowing what it is
you know. *I cannot quite recall*, we say,
speaking on behalf of a fog that floats

rock, silk, and heroin across the ocean.
I cannot, says the wind, or some lost soul
who walks the earth, never touching down.

* * *

Where a mind divides, so too a hood
or national prayer breakfast where the word
love becomes a matter of contention.

We were born, after all, into the flesh
whose mission, like a meal, reminds us:
eat, sleep, tweet, do what you must do

to live. Like a gerrymandered district
or parish of dollars earmarked for promotion.
Small wonder we look up from pancakes

and prayer in disbelief at our poor choices.
I too feel lost, listening for the danger,
like any bank or church or living thing.

I feel this new and quiet desperation
enter the room, if only to whisper, *here
I am*. Like a phantom limb, *here, here*.

                    * * *

I love the tenor of talk in the morning
café where I drink mine black and read,
in the news, that scientists have found

a little cavern in the word *whole*,
it was there all along, unlike its cousin
complete, the entire room now full

of mouths opening and closing and if
you look down a throat, deep, you see
the shadow of the person in the name

and in the friend, once, whose pain was
so singular the doctors could not get
their scope past the scarring of the wine.

They could not tunnel to the issue, and so
he sighed, relieved, his whole body relaxed,
then fell back into darkness once again.

                    * * *

When I find our congregation online,
the swastika sprayed across the playground,
I know, the new proximities are here.

The velocity of money and bad ideas,
they feed a conflagration of stars, crosses,
fast machines, and plow them into crowds.

I too lost a friend in Pittsburg to talk
so deadly it turned into a man, a creature
of garbled anger in the chatroom dark.

The new proximities travel at the speed
of bullets stripped of jackets and the chamber,
the new noosphere an aurora of texts

around a planet that does what planets do,
what bodies do when a stranger enters
shul to wipe the faces from their bones.

* * *

Dear puritans of a perfect social order,
I too have felt distracted at the party
that is, granted, one imperfect space.

Ever the guy who reddens with important
views, or waxes on about their dull
vacation, but hey, we are forgiving here,

a bit messed up and grateful to be safe.
Policemen of the human heart, thank you.
You deserve a break, so take one. Please.

I will remember fondly your vigilance.
I will see myself in you, and then. I won't.
Because we are just unspeakably different

and lay our sacks of skin into dreams
that are genuine, odd, or odd enough
to reach the unheard voice and whisper, *yes*.

* * *

The pursuit of happiness makes time
a blur of consequences, as heaven is
for one believer, and utopia for others.

In other words, an idea, like a house:
in this life, we say. Or *are you happy,*
when it feels small to answer, *yes* or *no.*

Tonight, I learned a great woman died,
a nurse who caught the fever of a patient,
and I wonder how she felt about a world

she left untouched, unfinished and afraid.
Every day will be the one she missed,
the deed undone, the calling she passed on.

Every year will bring the hour she changed
the bedpan of another, in a white room
called happiness, in which she disappears.

* * *

Here, between abysses of enormity
and the quantum small, a child is born.
A figure so intricate we cannot see

where matter ends, life begins, a body
stands to walk from evolution's flow chart
into a room, late, with a table, a lamp,

a sheet of paper, a hearth for the fire
to lay the skeletons of last night's dream.
The new sublime is a place like this,

an abyss that eats the sun and grass.
I have traveled a great distance to arrive
here, in this garden of black flowers, to say,

I am sorry, to the widow on behalf
of no one, nothing, everything, death,
the part gone speechless for whom I speak.

* * *

The abyss of synthesis, de Chardin
called it, the dark and darker labyrinth
you see wherever you see life, as if,

through the lens of a new science set
to music, we could fall in love again,
revive, in our basilica of nerves,

the marriage of mind to some first star,
here, in a coffee shop named *Aura*.
An abyss of design so fine, it opens up

the O's of awe in holy counterpoint.
But what of the maze that lies there still
when the eye closes. The veil of flies

descends. Cats wander the empty house.
What of the kilowatt that cannot kick
a stone-white heart back into the world.

* * *

When I first saw the Sistine Chapel,
I saw a great room inside a smaller.
I saw a god inside the need for god,

and so, one man, high in the scaffolds,
on his back and painting the flesh tones
of lovers into us, their afterlife.

I took them home, reimagined them
whenever I speak of gods and angels.
Call paradise a bridge over waters

in whom the shadows of the girders float
and lay a cooler weather on the river.
I too have felt that from a stranger.

I have heard a radio playing in a far
room a cheerful and infectious tune,
though I cannot find that room, not yet.

* * *

Dear philosopher of the noosphere,
I love you. And I worry about the axis
of pure white light driven through the planet,

how we breathe it when we whisper: *love*.
I want to believe in the evolution
of kindness, that it grows more and more

complex in its affections for the strange.
The problem with paradise is the one
good bar where each is every, plus one.

But we live in uncertain times. Therefore
tyrants, purges, plagues that quarantine
our angels. Yes, I know. You are dead.

But stay in touch. All that is beautiful
bespeaks a bit of chaos. Text me. Call.
For we are different, thank the stars. Between us.

* * *

When Lao bid farewell to Confucius,
he said, *Friend, go easy on the dogma.
Remember, laws create the criminal.*

But if laws are bad, what of the lawless
precincts of criminals at war, the lions
at heart who unhinge the prison gate.

Precisely, said Lao, *the mind at war.*
What of the bitter narcissist in office,
the bully, the baby, the wall, the eternal

disappointment who could not please his father.
Seek the lowest places, Lao said.
Be like the river as it falls. And then

he left. And between philosophers,
a tenderness opened. A prison filled.
The blood of millions wandered to the sea.

* * *

*No evolutionary future awaits except
in association with everyone else.* I read
that once. I was hoping for a picture.

I was hoping for a speaker just close
enough, in the sweet spot of the seen.
The icon of my Christ links to Virgil

to Jove. The spirit of each is none alone.
Like earth that way, aflame in the eyes
of machines, and our eyes looking back.

When I look back, when de Chardin looks
my way, I feel a little powerless,
pointless, like clicking *like* beside a fact,

as if it needs me. It needs more friends
and feels nothing. No favorite, no cold.
I google *everyone,* and my cursor freezes.

* * *

To touch the untouchable, our hands,
invisibly inked, pressed into a record
no one reads, each anonymous labor,

each microscopic kindness or mistake,
scattered in one continuous departure,
is this what we want, to be everywhere

and nowhere, always dissolving, always
arriving, leaving like faces in the mirrors
of the nursing home. Always in the air,

ashes from a mountain, long repressed,
falling as a coastal rain, without sound,
and you feel it, smell it, the small winged

consequence of everything, and nothing
untainted, undisturbed, and the smoke
in your eye turns to water, and you follow.

* * *

Long ago, de Chardin dreamt he would
die one Easter, and, indeed, he did.
He loved the iconography of ending

with a question. And a room of heads
would nod to hear a query rise, like balloons
across an April lawn in the silence after.

But that is another story. What I mean
to say is. He was talking with a friend.
Before he died, he reddened with wine,

toasting time as a journey toward a chat
like this. And then his arm went numb.
His chest ached. His friend got up to catch

the man who fell like a dime in a fountain.
It was just that quick, and like a friend,
the whole sky broke. And took the silver in.

* * *

Something for the ferry, for the moon
laid down across the eyelid of the sun.
Something for the garden to comfort

the beloved arranged in neighborhoods
named for the faith of lives who visit.
Something for a name engraved against

the quiet of the yard, the hollow place
burrowed through the halo of the grass.
Something for those who wait for the rest

of night to carve its passage and withdraw.
Some grief is slow to make its way in,
slower still to fade. How strange this gift,

this earth we leave the moment that we enter,
this pain so deep it feels no pain, not yet,
this stone that breaks the circle of the sun.

* * *

Most of what we dream is dreamless.
A window on an emptiness, a womb
of stars. Who can tell us otherwise.

Long ago my mother lay quietly dying
beneath the dove of the morning news.
We came together, my sisters, my brother,

me. We were confused like the rooms
of Los Angeles when the power goes,
when streetlamps sink into one black pool.

We slept, if we slept, in shifts, laughed
the odd, cautious laughter of the grieving.
But I recall a distance among us, unlike

all others. Something my mother said,
when I was not listening. And it just kept
calling, small and trembling. Like a star.

POEMS

Amanda Auchter

POEM IN WHICH ST. MARIA GORETTI GIVES LILIES TO HER MURDERER

In 1902, Alessandro Serenelli tried to rape 12-year-old Maria Goretti. He struck her with an awl fourteen times, killing her. He later claimed to have had a vision of Maria in his jail cell holding fourteen lilies. She is considered the youngest saint.

Do not think I didn't hear you
call for me when I sat at the top of the stairs

mending shirts. A child –
two braids, a pink skirt,

my mouth filled with hymns,
honeysuckle, soup.

And you with your fist   my hair
in your fist

no.

I am not you, so sorrowful, face
pressed to the stones. I am not

you, mouth of dirt and cobwebs.

But here is my fist of lilies. Here,
another bouquet I place

in your hand. Watch it brighten,
then

Amanda Auchter is the author of *The Glass Crib* (Zone 3 Press, 2011) and *The Wishing Tomb* (Perugia Press, 2012). Her poems have appeared in *The American Poetry Review*, *North American Review*, *Shenandoah*, *Tahoma Literary Review*, and the Academy of American Poets' *Poem-a-Day* project.

ignite its flame. See
how it crackles   how you

        crackle

into the fire, smoke. You, soot-
    swaddled. I bring you flowers,

clean them against your eyelids. Forgiveness
    is fire, flower. Listen –

        the song inside your body, pulse
of white. Hold out your palms. Find it there.

Meryl Natchez

THE TENTH TIME

Nirvana is here, nine times out of ten—
Hô Xuân Hu'o'ng

The disposable diaper
in the meadow

The morning at the DMV

The razor wire on top of the chainlink around the
concrete
around the school

For every black man in college
five behind bars

What happens to the eyes
as the argument flares

The blueprints for the gas chambers, meticulously filed

The invasion

The story of the invasion

The story behind the story
of the invasion

The ones who knew to profit
from it

Meryl Natchez is the author of four poetry collections, most recently *Catwalk* (Longship Press, 2020). Her work has appeared in *Los Angeles Review of Books*, *The Hudson Review*, *Poetry Northwest*, *ZYZZYVA*, *Literary Matters*, and *The American Journal of Poetry*.

Mariella Nigro
(Translated by Jesse Lee Kercheval
and Jeannine M. Pitas)

THE DARK AIR

But the cone of light is reversed
illuminating the tunnel of the past
the remote, the old, the real, the stuff of dreams,
time compressed to a mere instant
space to a point
beautiful black hole

and wells appear
luminous pools
full of little frogs and paper boats
into which we dipped our palms
splashing childhood joy

and the shadow of those eucalyptus trees
shaped like summer
with the bush stretching its arm
so we could reach the last low-growing flower
and the glimmer of snails
threaded and hung around our necks

and we, such sisters, dancing
in winged white sandals of October
colored ribbons through long hair
playing *Ring around the Rosie*

Mariella Nigro of Uruguay has published eight books of poetry and two of literary essays, most recently *Frida y México: de visiones y miradas* (Yaugurú, Montevideo, 2017). In 2011, she received the Bartolomé Hidalgo Poetry Prize and in 2013, the Morosoli Prize, both honoring her complete poetic work. Jesse Lee Kercheval and Jeannine Marie Pitas are poets and widely-published translators of work by South American poets.

and the impossible shade
barely a flash of darkness
unsuspected gamble
in the death's invisible face.

Alexandra Teague

THE ROUGH BEAST NEVER ASKED TO BE BORN

which is what all teens say at some point on some angry
street corner, sweating in unfashionable culottes, blaming
their parents for their stunted sense of style, their everything-

wrongness, as Paris swarms like a million bees from the hive
of *inaccessible* and *born to this* and *sleek* around their bad-permed
hair. And they are not lying: none of us asked to be the frizzled

flower of ourselves, the slow galumph, the beasty morning breath
and clawing forward over clumps of emails, all of them flagged
in small, stiff importance like the campus lawn each spring

when a pro-life sorority plants pink plastic flags to remember
fetuses who didn't ask to be born but also didn't ask *not* to be:
the future staking wonder onto accident's soft turf. As if

it weren't always too late: this arriving at the party of ourselves –
Surprise! – in little Oshkosh overalls and *Born 2B Cute* shirts,
our lives underway before consciousness bothers to tell us,

so of course we feel swamp-skinned and blush-faced to say
what we're doing here. Like my friend's thirteen-year-old son,
when my friend, his mother, fainted during a dog walk, leaned

over her to say "Mom, can you please stop doing that? It's *so*
embarrassing." Meaning, if I never asked for my body to be here,
I doubly didn't ask for yours with its menorrhagia and aging mother-

---

Alexandra Teague is the author of three poetry collections from Persea Books: *Mortal Geography* (2010), *The Wise and Foolish Builders* (2015), and *Or What We'll Call Desire* (2019). She is also the author of the novel *The Principles Behind Flotation* (Skyhorse Publishing, 2017).

ness. I never asked to climb down from the Spanish moss of nothing:
to cross the slouchy sand dunes, my feet leaving marks of excessive
beingness all over everything. I never asked for toxic wells, explosives

packed in trunks of cars, society's tidal pools sucking out, refilling,
and me, why? – *The future will fix it!* – left holding the toilet plunger.
As if kids aren't all questions, like *What rough world imagines a beast*
padding across the sands of time would be walking to its own birth?

Alexandra Teague

'THE ORANGE BLOSSOM SPECIAL' (ARRANGED FOR ROME'S BURNING)

I want you to hear the first notes when the fiddle
starts to sound like a train, though even then there's something
squawky to it, something donkey about the wheels

along the high thin trestle of the strings, though maybe
the bow is the trestle and the fiddle is the train upside down
in the dark of the tunnel, which is also the audience:

I want you to hear people in an Ozark theater clapping harder
as it bears down at them and the pink gel lights keep blooming,
and the woman dueling now with the man in the red silk vest

keeps carrying on, which is what we mean by a showstopper:
that it barrels toward us: screeching of wheels turning
in the air by her shoulder, her chin cupping a freight train

that must be a passenger train, aren't we all on it?
The fiddles fiddling as Rome, well you know what it does,
but it looks less like flames and more like sunset or Fire

in the Hole, a rollercoaster that dived in the dark in a mine
that was just a building built to look old-timey: thin plastic
fringe with orange lights shining behind, the pumped-in sound

of crackling. Hands in the air for a mine fire. Hands in the air
for the Baldknobbers with their black-horned masks and cut-
out eye holes, who set the fire, who no one mentioned then, set

the Ozarks on the tracks of whiteness. Hands in the air for
a family ride based on vigilantes, for a past that people
(some people) plunge into and come out laughing. It's what

the music of this country rushes from and keeps on playing:
one long track for a luxury liner called *The Orange Blossom*
Special that sped to Florida in the 1940s as white people

slept under white sheets like orange petals drifted from
groves to the sound of that rocking that's the sound of
this fiddling as the strings keep burning, as the fiddlers smile

in satiny ruffles. Didn't they back up the Nashville greats?
The program says so. The program's full of the near-adjacents.
Hands on its glossy paper if they might be your ancestors

who played on as the country burned and lights that said
Country burned, meaning something different or else the same
in a box called *entertainment.* Hands in the air if you grew up

near here, if you loved the magic shows, where tigers disappeared
from their cages and came back roaring. Hands in the air
if you fear the air here; if the stage has trapdoors; if the train

has trapdoors; if the fiddle keeps barreling; if the song's
familiar as it flattens you; as it whistles by you; as it does not
flatten you; if you know that dilemma of the trolley lever

that's really a train lever: whom do you save? Hands in the air
if it's not your choice. If it is your choice. If the trolley's
automated. If you're being held up; if the music keeps coming;

if the clapping's going to start now; if you don't want to hear
the foot stomp and popcorn rattle in this icebox theater; if
you're not immune to it; if you fear your own blood that ran

through your grandmother and her real father who beat his
wife back in West Virginia stone-cold dead, like they say,
though the body's not stone; it's more like a horse

before it turns into the hairs of a fiddle bow. Hands in the air
if there's blood all over them. If there's blood on his knuckles
in the gas station bathroom as he drives to Texas to fuck

his lover, so nine months later: your grandmother. Hands
in the air if the show is over; if the show's just starting; if
the parking lot lights keep fritzing like bug zappers; if no

one in your family's ever been to Rome, just the Olive
Garden in Paris, Texas. Hands in the air if you'd like more
breadsticks. If Rome's being redlined. If this ride's

too violent. If you'd like to ask the dead some questions. If
you can hardly hear yourself. If the train that's not a train
is screeching closer, whistling and wheedling as the emcee's

saying *Wow, folks! Have you ever heard a fiddle sound like that?*
Did a train just go right through our hearts, or what? Well, give it up!

Jenna Le

GUARDIAN ANGEL

In my room full of phonograph trumpets,
I listen for one voice from miles far off
to rise above the rest: your voice. Then I become

the owl I am and, using earth's magnetic field
to guide me, I fly into your mouth, make your palate
vibrate with the whoosh of my wings,

I tangle in the windsock
of your breathing, I am the brown paper bag
in which you bury your head

to avoid hyperventilating,
I tango with your throat
until the carbon dioxide you exhale

makes a mist that wipes clean your memory
of ever having not been enough,
of ever having been anything other than deserving.

Jenna Le is the author of the poetry collections *Six Rivers* (NYQ Books, 2011), *A History of the Cetacean American Diaspora* (Indolent Books, 2017), and *Manatee Lagoon* (Acre Books, 2022). Her poems have appeared in *AGNI, Denver Quarterly, Los Angeles Review, The Massachusetts Review, Michigan Quarterly Review*, and *Pleiades*.

Emily Schulten

DE COLORES

Mother's Day, 2019

When my husband left that morning
I'd only just started losing the baby

that wasn't even really a baby yet –
it was just growing a tail, something

else we cannot keep. He was getting
into a van to drive to Homestead

to sing in Spanish to children being held
in the migrant detention center.

Their hands, he said, made shadows
against the tarp-covered fence –

in shapes like forming souls, perhaps –
while he followed a procession

of the helpless, for the helpless,
and I laid beside the dining room table

on the cold floor where I convalesced
in the warmth of loss and wept, our dog

licked my salt face, and when I shook
it felt as if it was the actual earth shaking,

Emily Schulten is the author of two poetry collections, *Rest in Black Haw* (New Plains Press, 2009), and *The Way a Wound Becomes a Scar* (Kelsay Books, 2021). Her poems have appeared in *Ploughshares, Tin House, The Massachusetts Review*, and *Prairie Schooner*.

the whole world mourning tiny voices
that've been made silent, made hard to find,

and while I shook he sang, *de colores*
son los mil reflejos que el sol atesora.

Jason Tandon

BECAUSE THERE WAS NOTHING

Because there was nothing
I could say
or write,
no amount of flowers
I could send

I gave my friend a
poem a thousand
years old
and translated, no less,

and after he read it aloud
to his wife and son, he
stood up from the
kitchen table,
scattered feed for the chickens outside

and noticed in the dimmed
light how tall the grass had
grown.

Jason Tandon is the author of four books of poetry, most recently *The Actual World* (Black Lawrence Press, 2019). His poems have appeared in *Ploughshares, Prairie Schooner, Beloit Poetry Journal, North American Review*, and *Esquire*.

Deborah Brown

THE GLASS PARROT

I have never understood the way stars burst
apart. I am deaf to wind and trees
to the rose bush we planted, to the tomato plants
lying down with their fruits this August.

I almost understand – how St.Thomas More
became a fanatic and a torturer, and why young men
with hope and without it think a bomb is an answer.

I almost understand the day I was at your bedside
holding your child-sized hand. Tight in your other hand
the glass parrot. No – I made that up for the first poem
about your death.

There was no glass parrot. I did not
hold your hand. I stared at the cancer-filled mound
of your stomach, at your cheekbones that stood out
like wings, at your hand, really child-sized.
No, I don't understand.

Deborah Brown is the author of two collections of poems: *Walking the Dog's Shadow* (2011), and *The Human Half* (2019), both from BOA Editions. Her poems have appeared in *Margie, Rattle, Stand, Mississippi Review*, and *The Pushcart Prize* anthology.

Emily Franklin

ANOTHER DEDICATION – AFTER CZESLAW MILOSZ

He said the dead could come
disguised as birds

so I wait for finches to flit
across the panes, landing

on rhododendrons opening
sticky and pink or the bulbous junco

bird of the ground, with its receding shades
of gray, dark-eyed and seed-driven, perched

long enough that I dare to ask aloud are you
my friend who died young come back

for a round of lawn tag or could you be
that one I kissed who, barefoot, rang the doorbell

so many times and at seventeen I thought this
romantic and we kissed on someone else's stoop,

nesting there just for a few hours and he called
and called again and I did not call back –

not right away and then one spring I did
and learned he'd gone and though I was

Emily Franklin is the author of the poetry collection *Tell Me How You Got Here* (Terrapin Books, 2021). Her work has appeared in *The London Sunday Times, Guernica, The Cincinnati Review, New Ohio Review, The Baltimore Review,* and on National Public Radio.

an adult I ached for my teenage self and for him
and his fine, soft hair, and those faded

jeans and how in the magnolia trees some bird
shat on the sidewalk as we'd huddled there

and now it could be him or you or anyone dead
at the window, glad for the black

sunflower seeds poured into the feeder
as though I have more to offer and can hold

my hand out to call the dead back as though
by feeding them I could save them.

Sara Henning

A BRIEF HISTORY OF HURRICANES

As Hurricane Laura rages toward the heel of Louisiana's boot, we watched a
    coroner wheel

    our neighbor out of his front door on a gurney.
            With his body went the whole alphabet of the world.

We stood there, husband, staring through blinds, embarrassed we didn't know his
    name. The stars,

    they're dead before their light ever reaches us.
        His living room, dark save for a single torchiere,

its sprawl of glow bleeding out. I want to know why darkness can be interrupted
    by the idea of a star,

    as if time never existed. Time, it slips within me – my mother's blood, my
        father's blood, blood

of a whole generation – that furious haunting.
    My aunt's double-wide clutched up by Hurricane

    Andrew. My mother planking windows to   quash the electric hymn
        of water, skin,

David shelling Savannah with my father's fury. You stayed up, husband,
    waiting for the strike –

    horror, water, an eye which spares us.
        But I'm lost in sleep's turbine, images

Sara Henning is the author of the poetry collection *View from True North* (Southern Illinois University Press, 2018). Her poems have appeared in *Quarterly West, Crab Orchard Review, Witness, Crazyhorse, Meridian,* and *The Cincinnati Review.*

of our neighbor spliced against my aunt's Schnauzer,
    the one she left in a moment's flash,

        hurling his scrawny body at their trailer's door.   I wonder if
        she's haunted by his bark

twisting through metal as her children
    sprint for the car, no room for him among

      heaps of clothes, Wolf's chili cans, wedding photos,   piles of
what she could carry.

In my dream, my neighbor has risen above   the rage of any water.

Robin Chapman

AT THE BEACH THE SUMMER MY MOTHER FILES FOR DIVORCE, DECIDING, AFTER THREE YEARS, MY FATHER HAS LEFT FOR GOOD

Watching the waves come in
it's not their metronomic repetition,
    slightly a-kilter in the swell
if you're a surfer, but the subtle
    shifts in rhythm of foam-spill,
sand-spit, light-strike, running out
    to sea again or swirl – I waited,
a fourteen-year-old girl on the edge
    of adolescence, beachcombing
sunny days at the Atlantic shore,
    for their long wash back to catch
the sand fleas as they rose and fed
    in the pebbly trough and dug
back in as the receding surf
    sucked our sandcastle's turrets
down into its moat – the way
    you'd feel them scrabbling
in your hands as if you held a wave –
    the scene somehow reminiscent
of a book my father read to me long before –
    how the first of the five Chinese brothers
could swallow the ocean
    and spit it back – though that
must have meant to translate tsunamis
    into a story you could tell a child.

Robin Chapman is the author of 10 books of poems, most recently *The Only Home We Know* (Tebot Bach, 2019). Her poetry has appeared in *Valparaiso Poetry Review, The Hudson Review, Poetry East,* and on the Academy of American Poets' *Poem-a-Day* project.

Julie Danho

CNN SAYS NUCLEAR WAR COULD BREAK OUT AT ANY MOMENT

but I'm taking my daughter to math club
      because she loves playing Moneybags
and Sum Swamp and Smath, which is
      just Scrabble looted and repackaged

for math fans. Bombs are math too, half-lives
      and chain reactions. Decades ago,
my mother was drilled to duck under
      her desk, protect her face and neck,

but do I tell my daughter to take cover
      or flee for better shelter? A scientist
could reduce the decision to equations
      lovely as calligraphy until the translation

(fallout dose, transit time). Her bomb may be
      smaller than the one my mother
waited for. A mile beyond its blast, she might
      survive. As she leaves the car,

I hand her a backpack filled with stickers
      and glitter markers. We have it easier
than so many. It's raining, and her umbrella
      springs into a bunny, its ears up, alert.

Julie Danho is the author of the poetry collection *Those Who Keep Arriving* (Silverfish Review Press, 2020), and a chapbook, *Six Portraits* (Slapering Hol Press, 2014). Her poems have appeared in *Pleiades*, *New Ohio Review*, and *Bennington Review*, as well as featured on *The Writer's Almanac*, *Poetry Daily*, and *Verse Daily*.

Megan Gannon

DISPATCH FROM THE EVENTS LEADING UP
TO THE END

Because you asked the baby's sister and brother to watch him
while you showered – 15 minutes, max. Because at first you

were annoyed to find the baby's brother had gone outside,
before remembering how many car trips he'd been tasked

with cajoling the baby through crabbiness. Because
the baby's sister would, on such occasions, burrow deeper

into her nest in the back-backseat, unhearing. Because when you
retrieved the baby after your shower, his sister did not look up

from her phone. Because you asked the baby what he had
in his mouth right before he began choking. Because

you fished from his mouth maybe a dozen dark, jagged stones.
Because you do not keep such stones in the house.

Because later that night the baby's sister informed
the baby's parents that the baby had been eating rocks.

Because when you asked the baby's sister why
she hadn't prevented the baby from eating rocks, she swore

in the same breath that she didn't know, that the baby's brother
had told her. (Because the baby's sister is White,

Megan Gannon is the author of the poetry collection *White Nightgown* (Apprentice House, 2014). Her poems have appeared in *The Best American Poetry*, *Atlanta Review*, *Boulevard*, *Crazyhorse*, and *The Hudson Review*.

and his brother is Black.) Because you sat there listening
to her blame her mistake on the Black boy she lives with,

and you knew her father would say nothing.
Because you knew if you said something to the baby's sister,

that the baby's father would yell at you for upsetting her.
Because you sat there, rage funneling into a dark, hard pit.

Because the next day you left and took the boys with you.
Because the next day a White woman walking her dog

in Central Park was asked by a Black man to leash her dog.
Because in a city of six million people, where a man is trying

to find a sliver of quiet in which to hear a bird's dark, jagged call,
this seemed a reasonable request. Because the White woman

did not appreciate the correction. Because the White woman
called the police. Because the White woman told the police

that an African American man was threatening her.
Because the White woman knew she could pin her own

poor behavior on the Black man and come out clean – oh so
lily white. Because rage seeped from your pores like rancid onions

for weeks. Because *personal* and *political* begin and end the same way.
Because this story always begins and ends the same way.

Because the White woman learned her behavior somewhere.
Because she learned her behavior under your roof.

Peter Krumbach

BIRDS DON'T UNDERSTAND US

A woman on the park bench opens her husband's head. There's
another head inside your head, she announces. Well, open it,
instructs the husband. The woman reaches in, extracts a
rosary, a fungo bat, and then, straining, hauls out the man's
mother. To the Mississippi kite, balanced on the tip of the
oak's highest branch, this doesn't make sense. It preens its
belly, little orgasms rippling the feathers. A slice of its mind
signals fulfillment. One eye on the scene below, the other
turned inward, the kite pictures lizards and mice regurgitated
into the beaks of its young. I told you, Friedrich, shouts the
woman as the couple switches positions. Now the man
inspects the wife. A column of warm air rises from the
meadow. With two strokes of its wings, the kite's adrift in the
current. Gliding off, it finds itself soothed by the shriek
escaping its throat. From the distance, it hears the husband call
out the items pulled from the woman's head –
Hypothalamus! Marzipan! Don Giovanni! What's this?

Peter Krumbach's poems have appeared in *Copper Nickel, DIAGRAM, Hobart, The
Manhattan Review, Sixth Finch*, and *Washington Square Review*.

Mar Ka

FROM WHERE I FLEW

with acknowledgement to Tyree Daye's poem "From Which I Flew"

only alone quickly in silence could I go from a home fortified against ghosts
the spirits of the Tsars and Stalins of the earth

told to keep my head down   follow the rules   don't rock the life-boat

we lived then in a Chicago neighborhood
where we could make the sign of the crucifix
openly on the street speak whatever
in whatever language we wished
facing only a bit of name-calling   hiring prejudice

how many storks does it take to bring spring to Eastern Europe?

I have nowhere to go but I leave anyhow
driving my American station wagon west   and when they ask why
well I say I no longer believe in the same God
as the rest

I can't be what I have to be to be there
I fail their test

and regret   it's a pair of frayed socks rolled up at the back of my sock drawer
a pair I wear only sometimes   while all the others are being washed

---

Mar Ka is the author of *Be-Hooved*, a collection of poems (University of Alaska Press Literary Series, 2019).

Nancy Miller Gomez

HOUSE OF FREAKS

Come closer.
This is where I get to be the person
I am. Odd and unnumbered.
My kitchen teeth. My sponge tongue.
My paper doll skin. Here is where
I unwind the coil
of my hands and string my bare
face up like a lantern. Look,
we're like a family of road flares.
Did we get your attention? See,
I'm shedding my last pair
of eyes. I'm not watching
the parade of strangers.
We have cotton socks
and warm soup and the sound
of helicopters circling has finally
faded back into the everyday hum.
We've stopped reading the papers.
Now we make up the headlines
we want to hear. News flash:
a garden snail is crawling
across the flagstone outside.
There is a hole in the word whole
you can fall into, and if
you're not careful, your sentences
can backfire like a muscle car
on the interstate of your mouth. If
you promise to wipe your feet

Nancy Miller Gomez is the author of the chapbook *Punishment* (*Rattle* chapbook series, 2018). Her poems have appeared in *Shenandoah, River Styx, The Massachusetts Review, American Life in Poetry, Verse Daily, The Best American Poetry,* and *Best New Poets.*

and shut the door you can
come in. Welcome.
You look like someone I once knew
who had a beautiful, two-sided smile.
See, already, you fit right in.

Carrie Shipers

OFFICE FAREWELL PARTY

We came mostly for the cake, which we found
dry and over-frosted, barely worth the effort
of leaving our desks.   If our *Congratulations*

seems a little strained, please blame sore throats
brought on by allergies, the HVAC spreading
spores again.   We agree the firm you're moving to

is excellent.   We've applied there, too,
but never had an interview.   When you offer
to pass along our names and résumés,

we recognize you're trying to be kind but know
you'll never follow through.   By the time
you finally feel secure enough to bring us up,

you won't remember why you wanted to.
We assure you the forgetting will be mutual.
Monday we'll be sad to see your empty desk,

the list of tasks you left without completing,
but despite our promises to keep in touch,
if you attempt to make a date we'll find excuses

to refuse.   We don't blame you for wanting
one last afternoon to reminisce, listen to
how badly you'll be missed.   When it's our turn

Carrie Shipers is the author of two chapbooks and four full-length collections, most recently *Grief Land* (University of New Mexico Press, 2020). Her poems have appeared in *Hayden's Ferry Review, New England Review, North American Review, Prairie Schooner,* and *The Southern Review.*

we'll surely want the same, and like you
we'll let ourselves forget how these send-offs end:
Once you exit with your personal effects,

leftovers we'll insist you take, you'll stop
existing as yourself and become just
one more person who abandoned us.

Brian Gyamfi

A POET TRAVELS TO THE SOUTH

There is no sunshine here; every child is afraid of the river.
There is no shadow here; every woman has a name on her arm

but is it Abraham or Kevin?

It is time for me to write to the councilmen.
But I have no time to do such things.
People of the Mississippi River, do you swallow the water?
There is fire on the surface and every man is swimming.
The toilet in the living room is filled with lilies and rosemary.

In one restaurant I found Jesus. In another,
a mobile phone. Hello, my visa is on fire.
My English is limited, but my friend speaks
it beautifully.
Let me give him the phone.

In Georgia, I met my wife at McDonalds; she had silicon breasts.
I read her a poem like a man biting on ice water.
Democracy is good. I take another flight to Baton Rouge
and spend three nights in New Orleans.

Why can't I apologize for my lies?
I am the son of half a geography.
The world is full of more lives than before.

But I can pause here, take a walk to the Museum of Bodies.
The commonwealth is a prejudice, a hoax. I

Brian Gyamfi is a Ghanaian-American poet at the Helen Zell Writers' Program at the
University of Michigan.

am a person of many languages.
I am not to be blamed for the fire

but I understand that the children are ants and are eaten by ants.
I take my wife to Landon; she wants to go back to Kenner.
I give my wife pizza; she thinks it is too salty.
Let's go to the zoo in Alexandria.
The elephant is young, the tiger is a buffalo.
My wife says no; take me to a better place.

Shall we proceed to go to another restaurant?
Can you sleep with the lights on?
Can you talk to your God?
There's no trolley from Monroe to New Iberia.

Susan Rich

COMPASS

Elizabeth Bishop often kept a compass
in her small jacket pocket: a little-known fact
about the poet who fell regularly from a delicate
map of sobriety, lost her keys, entire weeks –
even countries. Could a compass – initially used
in fortune telling, invented in the Han Dynasty – buoy
her with its divining arrow, its quivering and irregular
heartbeat? What are the coordinates of the soul:
mist-filled or incandescent, briny as ocean air or rugged
as Ouro Prêto? Bishop could lose herself in the architecture
of a bird cage, the clack of wooden clogs. But with binoculars
strung around her neck like miniature islands, a compass
in her hand, her brokenness could orient her, her brokenness
could console her like a harbor chart or a naked, pink dog.

Susan Rich is the author of five poetry collections, including *Cloud Pharmacy* (White Pine Press, 2014) and *Gallery of Postcards and Maps: New and Selected Poems* (Salmon Poetry, 2020). Her poems have appeared in *Harvard Review*, *New England Review*, *Gettysburg Review*, *TriQuarterly*, *Antioch Review*, and *O, The Oprah Magazine*.

Jessica Tanck

MAGNETIC NORTH

*Nature had here no monument to denote the spot which she
had chosen as the centre of one of her great and dark powers.*
– Commander James Clark Ross

1

The compass-needle swims circles.

It was a victory
but imagine how the world must've felt

cracked: the sun splitting, navigation shot.
And the men walked up into night:

twisting wings
of acid green. Unreal current, celestial tease,

so much light a trick
to me – illusion,

a fork
of mockery, nothing more

2

sinister. Weeks remain until I move west.

I keep finding glass in my feet. *Austere*, a friend
describes it: the backdrop of mountains, desert –

Jessica Tanck's poems have appeared in *Kenyon Review, Blackbird, Colorado Review, DIAGRAM, Meridian*, and *Ruminate*.

winter smog & wide, diagrammed streets. I brush
out the glass, dab at beads of blood. My friend reminds me

much of taste is memory, much of want a wound.
Truth is, I've started to crave it, ask:

what is familiar. Men watched
those needles skitter & turn, knew

what it felt like to stand at the center holding
an instrument that insisted:

you are lost.

Jessica Greenbaum

EACH OTHER MOMENT

We turned location back on.
We were resetting our passwords.
We were scanning the QR code
to order an iced matcha latte.
We were on hold; we were saying
representative into the phone.
We were showing our Excelsior Pass
and putting in our contact information
for timed tickets to the gardens.
We were signing up for a streaming
service and decrying our Zoom
appearance. We were skimming
not reading. We were trawling
and scrolling. We were calculating
the millennia before reefs could
revive and species come back
in colors we haven't imagined.
We were guilty, and each other
moment, also innocent. We were
meditating so the unforgiving
might give a little. We were trying
to find the contact information
for the company. We were
wondering where to recycle
foam rubber. We were listening
to a podcast and downloading
a playlist. We cross-indexed our

Jessica Greenbaum is the author of three poetry collections: *Inventing Difficulty* (Silver-fish Review Press, 1998), *The Two Yvonnes* (Princeton University Press, 2012), and *Spilled and Gone* (University of Pittsburgh Press, 2019). Her poems have appeared in *The New Yorker, Poetry, The Yale Review, Plume,* and *The Paris Review.*

top issues in Charity Navigator.
We were making suggested
go bags and stay bins for the likely
floods and fires. We were
wondering why men only
gave us one star. We looked to
the sky for how to help any
anything at all. We hit retweet
on the full moon and we liked
the Big Dipper. Constellations
etch-a-sketched the night, then the
window shade's round pull
rose into a sun and light came on.
We agreed with the ancients;
that was hopeful. We turned location
back off. We were innocent but
each other moment we were lost.

Brent Ameneyro

TO MY ANCESTORS

We've grown about four inches over the last
one hundred and fifty years (I thought you'd like

to know). We've made these weapons that
could end all life (sorry). We carry candlelight

in our pockets. Well, I can't explain it all,
but there's a sense the end is near.

My friend (may I call you that? The salt
of the earth), I want to know the things you feared,

I want to know if anything has changed.
Have we always been such simple water

creatures grabbing anything in reach, scared
the sun will suck us into the sky? My father

doesn't like to talk about what's gone,
that's why I hide you under my tongue.

Brent Ameneyro's poems have appeared in *The Iowa Review*, *Ninth Letter*, *The Journal*, *Azahares*, and *Hispanic Culture Review*.

Allison Akootchook Warden

portal traveler

these future days
she watches through portals
flashbacks to the 80s
the time when
the Elders glowed
nightlights
sitting near one
like soaking up
an entire library section
on grace
if I could only reach through

the screen

to touch
the *sini*
of their sunshine ruff parkas
that would be
(the infusion)
of the long long long long ago
a swift-kick
dance
back
into how they kept
the earth steady
under their feet

Allison Akootchook Warden is an Inupiaq traditional artist. Her book of Twitter poems "TAIMANISAAQ/AKKUPAK (the long long ago/right now) was published by the Anchorage Museum in 2017. Her poem "we acknowledge ourselves" was recently featured in *Poetry* and on its podcast series.

Sibongumusa Ncube

WHEN HOME SAYS STAY

after "Home" by Warsan Shire

home pleads with you on hands and knees
to not walk out the door and then
home reminds you that your umbilical cord
is buried in the backyard,
as is your father's and that of his father
so when you walk into the storm
you will be untethered from the harbor

home switches tactics to get you to stay and
she calls you ungrateful
for wanting the green fields across the sea
instead of the warm but barren land that raised you
and the growl of your empty stomach cannot silence her because
you're not hungry, she argues, you're greedy
for always wanting more and more
and with a wagging finger she announces that
you may drink all you want from the golden well
but your thirst shall never be quenched

home watches you swap the land of your ancestors
and leave empty cupboards for first world plenty
and lay your identity at the *eGoli*[1] alter
but she's lost too many of her children to cry for you
so she turns back to sit by the hearth and wait
for the foreign land to spit your remains out
so she can bury you in the backyard

Sibongumusa Ncube attends Africa University and lives in Gwanda, Zimbabwe.
"When Home Says Stay" is her debut publication.

where your umbilical cord is buried
with your father's and that of his father
and tether you *emhlabathini*[2]
the only home you'll never leave

April 2022 Alaska/Zimbabwe

NOTES

The italicized words are written in isiNdebele, a Southern African language predominantly spoken in Zimbabwe and in parts of South Africa by people from the Ndebele tribe.

1. *eGoli*, "city of gold," is used as an idiomatic expression to describe moving to a place with better opportunities.

2. *emhlabathini* – "in the ground."

John Bargowski

ancestry.com

Suspected of copping
some horn player's sax
from the backstage
of a toney mid-town club,
a tenor worth more than a grand
headlined the sepia-stained article
some distant relative posted
to the family tree, so I'm straining
today to hear my uncle solo again
in a furnished room over
a garage on Baldwin,
him with that brass neck
and tapered body that bought him
another trip up the river,
tapping time with his boot
while his chapped hands
fingered the mother of pearl
inlays on the disks of the keys,
trying to blow those blue
notes he'd devoured slopping
dishes clean at the club's sink,
and string them together
into a melody I might recognize
years later, uncle buffing the mouth
of the sax's golden bell
so the light from his bare 60 watt
melted into its buttery glow
before he nested that horn
in a padded black case.

John Bargowski's most recent poetry collection is *American Chestnut* (Stephen F. Austin State University Press, 2021). His poems have appeared in *Poetry, Ploughshares, New Ohio Review, Gettysburg Review*, and *Prairie Schooner*, and on *Poetry Daily*.

Stephen Ackerman

FATHER, TIME

What if there were no earth? What if there were clouds,
And the clouds held rain, released the rain, and the rain
Kept falling –
Endlessly, through the dark radiance of space,
From galaxy to galaxy, the way a man weeps
At his own destruction?

There was the night I was home from college, winter break
After my first semester, I was reading *Helter Skelter*,
My father at the office holiday party, my mother at home
To avoid my father's office flirtations, when the telephone rang.
I can't remember now whether it was the police
Or the hospital on the line, but my mother quickly dressed,
We left in the car for the hospital after waking
One of my sisters, so they wouldn't awaken as orphans,
Wondering why they were alone, at night, no cars
In the driveway. The priest in the waiting room
Had given last rites to the couple in the other car,
And I remember the shock of that, that we wouldn't
Slough this off like a hangover that you wake to,
That fades by afternoon. My father was alive,
Scalped, but otherwise strangely unbruised.
Days and days we visited the hospital, holy days
And holidays, vigil through the anvil of those days,
Days we pounded ourselves into new shapes, days
Molten with fires fed by dread, the galaxies still wheeling
As they had since the beginning of time, but for us
Time had changed, the present veering out of control,

Stephen Ackerman is the author of the poetry collection *Late Life* (Silverfish Review Press, 2022). His poems have appeared in *Boulevard, Partisan Review, Ploughshares, Plume, upstreet,* and on *Poetry Daily.*

The slow motion of a car spinning, while you sit,
Strapped, helpless, waiting, reeling toward the future.
Finally, my father woke, and when the nurse called us in,
She asked him who we were. "Some sightseers," he said,
As if we were there to see some natural wonder,
An eighth wonder of the world, a man alive. He'd lost
Our names in the days and nights of sleep; we discovered
Soon enough how much else he'd lost in the grove
Of wounded trees where the car sailed as if lifted
By invisible wings.
We still had hope then that our lives had not unalterably
Changed, that the promise about time
Healing wounds would hold true. It was not true.
I would drive on the road that led to my parents' house
And look at serene exteriors of the houses of neighbors
And because I knew the secrets of the lives
Behind the door I entered, knew that I could not know
Which housed knives that cut bread, which skin, which
Hands held guns, which other hands, who slept
Through the night, who kept close watch of the seconds,
Minutes, hours on the bedside clock.

I returned to college.
My father tried to return to work.
Once upon a time and a very fine time it was, my father knew
The complexities of radar systems and sonar systems.
He invited me to a business meeting in the city
Where I attended college. Though my presence was strange
And inappropriate, my father insisted. He was, he said, going to give
A presentation on the latest advances in telecommunications
Equipment. I sat at a table with my father and
His client. The tentacles of the accident
Were still stretching into the future, extensions of a hydra
Blindly searching for something to sting.
Then my father took from his briefcase
Two tin cans connected by a string. He lifted
One to my ear, one to his mouth.
And then he wept.

Sydney Lea

WHAT SHINES?

Astonishing, this never-ending effort
to have had a happy childhood. Why does it matter
now, why will yourself into all that forgetting?
She may have been a good mother – at least she tried.

Did she? Once again, you're the one who's trying.
You contend you do remember moments that glow:
You picture her standing one day in the snow, her teeth
in a chatter, no doubt, and yet she looked quite cheerful –

or she seemed to be trying. As you are. The teeth at least
were one good feature, radiant to the end.
You were poised at the top of a hill on a Flexible Flyer,
red sled that shone, your Christmas present at nine.

It may have brought you joy. You're trying to alter
the down-slope rush, to make it shiny too,
to forget the icicles of snot, the raw
fingers, chilblains. Pain. A father was there,

a good man, you've always believed, but who's now no more
than a specter, whose presence is no more advantageous
than on that day. Or was it of some avail?
You can't remember. You honestly can't remember.

Perhaps you just don't want to. You're doing well –
at least you're trying – with this, your obstinate bid

Sydney Lea is the author of 14 collections of poetry, including *Here* (Four Way Books, 2019), and a Pulitzer Prize finalist, *Pursuit of a Wound* (University of Illinois Press, 2000). He is also the author of nine books of essays, most recently *Seen from All Sides: Lyric and Everyday Life* (Green Writers Press, 2021).

to winnow the damage and see if there's anything more
than just the sorrow. Well, there were certain instants.

You say, *I remember stones*. You say, *I saw
a beach by moonlight*. And did those pebbles glint
like stars, as you insist? Are you quite sure
clouds never came to eclipse them? You keep on trying.

There's that pervasive gleam along the shore.
Then you take a step and suddenly there's nothing

Carolina Hotchandani

PORTRAIT OF APHASIA ON A PLUM TREE

Was it not then – as you reached for a word like a ball you'd kicked high
into the plum tree's grasp, and failing to seize it, said, *Forget it,*
so the word stayed   there
suspended with the overripe plums warming in the sun
beside the nest of a bird neither of us could name
(though the problem of forgetting was not mine) –
Was it not then that silence filled the space
where the word might have bounced   like this,   like here,   like so,
and I might have taken it up and passed it back to you?
The absence of your thought condensed into a pit (as of a plum) I swallowed,
till it burrowed in my chest like a solid thing a word
could almost name.

Complete your sentence I did not
as I thought of the ball perched high in the branches' leafy clasp –

– and I hoped its touch was soft, its grip
firm and unrelenting.

Carolina Hotchandani's poems have appeared in *AGNI, Beloit Poetry Journal, The Missouri Review, Plume, Prairie Schooner,* and *West Branch.*

Kareem Tayyar

MEMORY

it was one of those nights when the horses flew into the trees.
when birds grazed in dark pastures.

when rain fell from the moon
& the sky told anyone who would listen that she used to be a

river. you know the kind of night I'm referring to.

the ones where you fly instead of

walk, sing instead of speak, bloom

instead of sleep.

the kind of night that doesn't happen
nearly as often as you'd like it to,

& that always leaves you hoping
she'll take you with her when she
goes.

Kareem Tayyar's poetry has appeared in *Poetry, Prairie Schooner, Brilliant Corners*, and
The Writer's Almanac. He is also the author of a collection of short fiction, *The Revolution
of Heavenly Bodies & Other Stories* (J.New Books, 2022).

Hailey Leithauser

HEARTS AND ARROWS

Fair-haired, tubbiest of cherubs,
rain down your barbs!
Chubby-armed scion, wake me
again with whistles of dove wings,
sweet whistles, spine-shudders.
Roust me, I beg you, with breath-kisses,
rumors of missiles, sharp darts
of delirium, agonies steeper
than canyons and chasms,
than fathomless depth-dark
gulches of oceans.
Unmask and dethrone me;
paint a bright marksman's target
on the arch of my back and when
you have emptied your quiver,
when I am sufficiently punctured
and scored and you've gorged
on my heart, then
sing to me, Fat Boy, of
her silk. Order me slide my thigh
over hers and giggle her neck
like a tipsy milkmaid,
for on this night sat late at the crumbed,
wine-stained cloths of my table,
I am cooled as stone, and grown old,
and no longer babble of women.

Hailey Leithauser's poems have appeared in *32 Poems, AGNI, Plume, Gettysburg Review, Poetry, The Yale Review,* and three editions of *The Best American Poetry.*

Constance Crawford

HERA, IN HER 80S, SORTING PHOTOGRAPHS

I'll keep this picture, it shows a truth about me
that I want them to see, my children
and whoever else is interested.
I have not left my mark the way I'd hoped –
except of course on my successive houses,
my handsome, well-run houses.
But who knows who I am
and what I've been through? No one.
I was close to sixty here, after the children were gone
and I had time to read and think; dressed well;
my husband came in and saw me there
in the living room chair reading a book.
He had one of his precious cameras
with him. He aimed it at me and snapped the shutter –
even after everything we'd said that morning.
I remember it well. He knew I detest
having my picture taken.
This time I looked straight at the lens
and let it be myself it saw and recorded.
I should probably destroy this picture,
the hatred that pours out of it.
But, in a way, I like my looks, my skirt fits well
just to the knee. My good legs are crossed
and one blue and white spectator pump is off,
lying on its side. I like that touch.
I'm going to keep this picture
and let my eldest daughter find it,
loose in the box with no explanation.

Constance Crawford's poems have appeared in *Red Wheelbarrow,* and in the anthologies *The Place That Inhabits Us* (Sixteen Rivers Press, 2010) and *A Bird Black as the Sun: California Poets on Crows and Ravens* (Green Poet Press, 2011).

Eva Saulitis

LOVE IS WHAT THIS IS

Flocks of storm petrels
stippled the luminous pewter
surface of the Strait that day:
here and there, from a distance
dark ink spatterings on milk glass
He steered the boat close
to scatter them, just to see

the lifting of four hundred pearl-gray bodies
all at once, by four hundred pairs
of javelin wings. Their forked tails
scissored the skyline diving rods
the forked sticks Dowsers
hold out before them, searching
for water running below ground

just to hear
the noise of a stampede of wingbeats
four hundred barefoot children running
on hard, dry earth, kicking up dust
thumping like the heartbeats
of a band of wild horses,
amplified

The flock tilted then,
the bodies and wings

Eva Saulitis (1963–2016) was the author of the poetry collections *Many Ways to Say It* (Red Hen Press, 2012) and *Prayer in Wind* (Boreal Books/Red Hen Press, 2015). She was also the author of three books of non-fiction: *Leaving Resurrection: Chronicles of a Whale Scientist* (Boreal Books, 2008); *Into Great Silence: A Memoir of Discovery and Loss Among Vanishing Orcas* (Beacon Press, 2013); and *Becoming Earth* (Boreal Books/Red Hen Press, 2017). "Love Is What This Is" is published here for the first time.